"You need to fa...

"My life is my life, Sam, and no one is going to interfere in it. I think we should agree to disagree and go back to a business relationship."

Sam leaned back in his seat and laughed. "If you believe we can do that, you're in need of more help than I thought."

"This is not a laughing matter, Sam, I'm completely serious. I can't get involved with you. I *won't* get involved with you. Whatever happened yesterday was a mistake."

"Maybe it was a mistake, but it happened. It was also the most wonderful experience in my life, and you don't walk away from wonderful, Liana. I'm going to pursue you, whether you like it or not."

With love to my brother,
Wayne Griffin,
the photographer in the family

CARIN RAFFERTY
A Change of Seasons

Silhouette Sensation

First published in Great Britain in 1991 by Silhouette Books, Eton House, 18-24 Paradise Road, Richmond, Surrey TW9 1SR

© Linda Kichline 1990

Silhouette, Silhouette Sensation and Colophon are Trade Marks of Harlequin Enterprises B.V.

ISBN 0 373 58143 2

18 – 9104

Made and printed in Great Britain

Prologue

Having lived in the Andean mountain range of South America for more than forty years, Father Santos was convinced he'd seen every human suffering imaginable. But even he was startled by the apparition standing in the middle of this unnamed forgotten village on the edge of nowhere. His handful of parishioners were whispering of demons and devils as he walked through them, and when he finally came face-to-face with the object of their attention, he understood their fears.

The young woman's hair was matted and tangled, and every exposed portion of her body was scratched and swollen. Her clothes were torn and covered with blood—too much blood to have been released from her own wounds, he quickly noted—and she had of all things, a camera clutched in her hands.

But it was her eyes that gave him the urge to make the sign of the cross, for there was nothing reflected in their depths. If it hadn't been for the shallow rise and fall of her chest, Father Santos would have been convinced that she was dead.

He spoke, but she didn't respond. He touched her, but she didn't move. Realizing she was in a state of shock, he tried to pry the camera from her hands, but they were locked around it as if her skin was forged to its surface. He tried again, knowing that many of these villagers were still steeped in superstition, and they would consider the camera an evil tool. If he wanted their help in caring for the woman, he had to disarm her, so to speak.

Finally he managed to free the camera. The moment he did, however, he regretted it. The woman screamed "Bill" as if her very soul had been ripped from her, and then she slumped and fell to the ground at his feet.

Father Santos did make the sign of the cross at that moment and began to pray, for he was certain that the woman was dead.

Chapter One

Except for her eyes, she was the kind of woman to inspire poets to write verse, composers to write music, and ancient kings to war for her hand in marriage, Sam Dillon decided as he stared at the woman who'd just opened her front door.

Parted in the center, her dark brown hair was caught at her nape with a white ribbon, and fell to her hips. Her face had the delicately chiseled, aristocratic features of the goddesses in Greek mythology. Of average height, her body was slender, with traffic-stopping curves in all the right places. Her chocolate-brown eyes were huge and framed by lashes so long and thick that Sam wondered if the upper set tangled with the lower set when she closed them. Those eyes were devoid of life.

Sam actually considered the fact that she might be blind, but knew he was wrong when her gaze flicked over him. He had the feeling that in that momentary appraisal he'd been analyzed, categorized, and dismissed, and it irked him.

He waited for her to speak, but she just stood there looking at him through those unnerving eyes. After several seconds had passed, she leaned against the door frame of her home with a bored fluid grace that made Sam feel gangly and awkward. His annoyance increased.

"I'm Sam Dillon," he said when it became apparent that she had no intention of opening the conversation.

There was no response from her. Not even a muscle twitch.

Sam tried again. "I've written to you several times, and spoken to you twice on the telephone." Still nothing. His annoyance began to veer toward anger. "If it's not inconvenient, I'd like a moment of your time."

At least she moved. She pushed herself away from the door frame. Finally, she said, "Very well." Then she turned and walked away, leaving the front door open.

It wasn't the most conventional way to invite a vistor in, but Sam needed her help too badly to question her manners. He entered quickly, closing the door behind him.

As his gaze slid around her living room, he discovered that it was even more disconcerting than the woman. Everything was stark white, from the ceiling to the plush carpet. There was a small white-velvet sofa with a glass-and-chrome table positioned in front of it, and a matching white chair with a solid glass pedestal beside it, on which rested a white telephone. There were no pictures on the walls, no newspapers or magazines on the coffee table, no television or stereo system, and no knicknacks. There weren't even dust motes dancing in the sunlight streaming through the windows. Sam not only thought the room was strange, but wondered if he should remove his boots before stepping onto the carpet.

While he contemplated the issue, he watched his "hostess" walk through a door straight ahead of him. Just before she disappeared from sight, he noted that besides her jeans and body-hugging white sweater, she was wearing a pair of tennis shoes that looked as if they had dried mud on them. He left his boots on and followed her.

If he'd thought the living room was strange, he decided the kitchen beat it hands down. It was solid beige. Instead of a table and chairs, there was a beige restaurant booth against the wall. Again, there was nothing on the walls, there was nothing sitting on the counters, and the appliances looked as if they'd never been used. If Sam hadn't known for a fact that Liana Stevens had been living in this house for three years, he would have thought she'd just moved in and hadn't had time to get settled.

"Sit down, and I'll make you a cup of coffee," she told him.

Sam sat and curiously studied the woman as she removed a single cup coffeemaker from a cupboard and set it on the counter. It, too, looked brand new and unused.

As he watched her make the coffee, the word enigma came to mind. Neither the woman nor her home were what he'd anticipated. Until three years ago, Liana had been one of the best free-lance photographers in the country. She'd won numerous awards and received critical acclaim for her ability to capture emotion on film, whether it be joy or agony.

But it was her nature photographs that had brought Sam here. One of his most prized possessions was a set of limited edition photographs of endangered species, which she had donated to a wildlife foundation for fund-raising. Those photographs had cost him an arm and a leg, but they had been well worth the money.

The coffeemaker sputtered as it finished its cycle. Sam watched Liana retrieve a beige mug from another cupboard, pour the fresh brew into it, and carry it toward him. After placing the cup in front of him, she slid into the other side of the booth, her face as unanimated as a mannequin's.

"You didn't offer me cream or sugar," he said, experiencing an overwhelming need to taunt her, to try to make her exhibit some type of emotion.

Her expression didn't change as she said, "You're a 'drink it black' man."

It was true, and Sam resisted asking how she'd known as he sipped the coffee. "This is the best cup of coffee I've had in a long time. Aren't you going to join me?"

"I never drink coffee."

Well, so much for the amenities, Sam thought in disgust. He found himself concentrating on her eyes and wondering how anything so beautiful could look so empty. The fact that they did intrigued him. It also raised the question of how a woman who appeared emotionless could take photographs that made people experience a full gamut of emotions. She was an enigma, he reiterated to himself. He'd never met one before, and after meeting her, he wasn't sure he ever wanted to again.

"I suppose you know why I'm here," he said.

"To make another pitch," she replied.

Sam couldn't help it. He had to grin. "Yeah."

She folded her hands on the table. "I told you that I'm retired. I no longer take photographs."

It was the word "retired" that bugged Sam. She couldn't be more than thirty-two or thirty-three years old. He took a firm grip on his impatience. "I know what you said, but I thought if we talked in person, I might convince you to make an exception in this instance."

Determined to state his case before she had a chance to refuse him, he quickly continued, "As I explained before, my grandfather is eighty years old and dying. For the past sixty-two years he's gone up into the Rockies to commune with nature as it bursts into spring. This may be the last spring of his life, and since the doctors won't let him go to the mountains, I want to bring the mountains to him."

"And you want to do that by giving him photographs."

Sam nodded.

"Then buy yourself a camera. Any amateur photographer can take pictures."

"No," Sam said quietly but firmly as he met her blank gaze with a resolute stare. "I don't want to bring him pictures of the mountains, I want to bring him *the* mountains, and no amateur photographer can do that. Your photographs aren't one-dimensional, pretty pictures. They're three-dimensional works of art, and that's what I want to give him. I want him to feel as if he's there, as if he's experiencing the reality."

She didn't reply. Instead, she turned her head and gazed out the window. Sam had the feeling that she saw nothing that lay within her line of vision, and he found the sensation disturbing.

She continued to gaze out the window as she said, "I'm retired, Mr. Dillon. I no longer take photographs."

"Dammit, lady!" he exclaimed, unable to control his temper a moment longer.

At least she returned her attention to him, even if she did look as unmoved at his explosion as she had when she'd opened her front door and found him standing there.

Sam drew in a deep breath and let it out slowly. His blood pressure dropped a notch or two, but it still had a long way to go before it reached normal.

"Excuse my show of temper," he said evenly, "but I don't think you understand how important this is to me. My grandfather is the most decent, honest man I've ever known. If I can live my life half as well as he's lived his, I'm going to be damn proud of myself. All I want to do is give him something special, something that shows him how much I love him."

Sam would have sworn that he saw some emotion flicker across her face, but it happened so quickly that he decided he'd imagined it.

"What you want to do is commendable, Mr. Dillon, but I am retired. I no longer take photographs."

Sam felt a wave of frustrated defeat flow through him. He wanted to rail at her. He wanted to shake her. He wanted... Damn, he wanted to see her exhibit some feeling, no matter what it was! He drained the lukewarm coffee in his cup.

As he returned the mug to the table, he fixed her with another stare. Aware of the automatic blinking of his eyes, he waited for her to blink. He gave up when her eyes remained wide open after his third involuntary one.

The woman wasn't human, he decided. She was some kind of witch or ghost or something from another planet, but definitely not human.

He leaned back in the booth, reluctantly acknowledging that nothing he said or did was going to change her mind. She simply wasn't going to help him, and it was time he accepted that fact. But it didn't mean he had to accept it gracefully.

"I'm sorry I bothered you," he said, his sarcastic tone of voice belying the apology. "But before I go, I'd like to say that when you're old and dying, I hope someone has the compassion to do something special for you."

This time, there was a definite change in her expression, and Sam watched, mesmerized, as the corners of her lips tilted slightly. The hint of the smile promised to be as beautiful as the rest of her, but the promise wasn't fulfilled. The beginning smile died as quickly as it had been born.

"Save your hopes for someone who needs them, Mr. Dillon," she said in a soft monotone. "They're wasted on me, because I'm already dead."

IT WAS THE LOOK OF SHOCK on Sam Dillon's face that registered in Liana's mind. She felt a glimmering touch of rueful humor and was startled by it. For the past three years, she hadn't felt anything but listlessness and a fervent wish for death.

She regarded the man curiously. When she'd said that what he wanted to do for his grandfather was commendable, she'd meant it. She'd also meant it when she'd said she no longer took photographs. All her photography equipment was packed away in her basement and would remain there until the day she died.

As he continued to stare at her in shock, she saw the remnants of his anger and his hopes reflected in the depths of his eyes. They were beautiful, expressive eyes, she acknowledged, a pale green color that lightened and darkened with his moods. They also gave her the impression that it would be very dangerous to underestimate him.

She switched her attention to his hair, which was black with a smattering of silver running through it. It was moderately long at the top and conventionally short at the sides and back, and as he suddenly raked his hand through it, she watched errant strands tumble across his broad forehead. She had the oddest compulsion to reach out and smooth it into place. Two emotions in one day, she reflected. Amazing.

Ignoring the compelling urge to straighten his hair, she lowered her gaze to his face. His brows were elegant slashes, his lashes long and silky, and his nose was straight and narrow. She was fascinated by his sculpted cheeks which tapered to a jutting chin with a distinctive cleft in its center.

Though she was certain he'd shaved that morning, she could already see the shadow of a beard, and she was bewildered when her shutter-button finger began itching to take his picture. She tucked the traitorous finger against her palm as he overcame his shock and frowned at her.

It was a disconcerted frown, part chastisement and part concern, and Liana felt another glimmer of that rueful humor when she realized that the man was trying to figure out how to respond to her words. She decided to take pity on him. "Excuse the dramatics, Mr. Dillon. They were uncalled for."

"And I apologize for my rudeness. It was also uncalled for."

She nodded her acknowledgement of his apology, and Sam felt strangely honored by that simple physical act. If he'd been intrigued with her before, he was even more so after her claim of being dead. It wasn't her statement that shocked him as much as the perturbing feeling that it was true.

It was those eyes, he realized. Intuition told him that they hadn't always been lifeless, and he wanted to know what had happened to make them so. He also knew that the chances of him making that discovery were about as slim as his being able to take a trip to the moon.

"Would you like more coffee?"

Liana was as surprised by her offer as Sam was. She'd asked the question without even knowing she'd been thinking it. A nagging little voice inside warned her that she'd regret letting him stay, but for some unknown reason, she wasn't ready for him to leave.

"I'd love it," Sam responded quickly, sure that if he didn't, she'd withdraw the offer and ask him to leave. He knew he'd failed in his mission, but he was too fascinated with her to simply walk out the door.

Liana rose and walked to the coffeemaker. Absently, she watched the liquid drain through the filter as she mulled over the events of the last half hour. Her day had started out as any other, fraught with the leftover remnants of nightmares. Even her long walk through the rain-drenched streets of Denver hadn't been able to dissipate the effects of her haunted night. She'd returned, resigned to spending the day with her ghosts, only to have the doorbell ring.

It was odd, but she'd known the man standing on her front porch was Sam Dillon before he even opened his mouth. His tall, muscular body, clad in jeans, a chambray shirt, and a worn denim jacket, had the same leashed tension she'd heard in his voice when she'd spoken with him on the telephone. On the phone he'd sounded like a man who'd try to move mountains to get what he wanted. In the flesh he looked like a man who *would* move mountains to get what he wanted.

Her nerves had gone on red alert at the sight of him and insisted that she close the door in his face. However, instinct had told her that would only make him more determined to move the mountain in his way—that mountain namely being her.

Letting him in had been the better part of valor, just as asking him to leave now would be. She knew she'd convinced him that she wouldn't change her mind about his picture-taking expedition, so why was she making him another cup of coffee instead of tossing him out the door?

Because as long as he's here, the ghosts will stay away.

Liana was so caught off-guard by that inner response that she wasn't aware that Sam stood next to her. She let out a startled gasp when he touched her arm.

"I'm sorry. I didn't mean to frighten you. I thought I'd bring over my mug so you wouldn't have to make another trip,'' Sam said as he peered down at her through narrowed eyes.

When he'd approached Liana, he'd realized by her concentrated expression that she was lost in her thoughts. She'd suddenly gone pale, every drop of color draining from her face, and he'd automatically reached out to touch her, thinking she'd become ill. But as he now stared into her face, he realized that his assumption had been wrong, at least in the physical sense. He also felt as if he'd been delivered a blow to the stomach.

If he'd thought the lifeless look in her eyes had been bad, the look of torment now reflected in their depths was terrifying. He felt as if he were peering into the portals of hell, and two conflicting emotions flowed through him. The need to protect her warred with the need to repel her. Both feelings were so intense that they were polarizing each other, locking him into immobility. Before those needs could complete their battle of wills, Liana's eyes were fathomless again and she reached out and took his cup.

Liana regarded Sam warily when they returned to the booth. She was still rattled by that strange thought that had come from nowhere, and, as they had at the front door, her nerves went on red alert again when Sam cradled his coffee cup in his hands and studied her over the rim.

Until now, she'd been able to read his every thought, but his eyes, which had been so expressive before, were now shuttered and riveted on her. An involuntary shiver crawled up her spine as she recalled her earlier impression that it would be dangerous to underestimate him. She should have thrown him out the door when she'd had the chance. The mountain mover was back and she had a feeling he'd returned with a bulldozer.

The silence between them stretched. Though Liana was tempted to speak on several occasions to relieve the tension, she didn't, because she knew Sam was waiting for her to do just that. If she had any hope of winning this cat-and-mouse game, then she had to refrain from making the first move. She released an inward sigh of relief when Sam finally finished his coffee and set his cup down on the table.

She parted her lips to ask him to leave, but before she could speak, Sam said, "I just realized that I never told you how much I was going to pay you for this job."

Liana started to tell him that the money wouldn't make a difference, but her mouth dropped open in shock at the outrageous sum he nonchalantly quoted. Even her most lucrative free-lance assignments hadn't paid that much!

Sam smothered his pleased smile at her look of disbelief. At last he'd managed to get a human response out of her. Why hadn't he thought to offer money in the first place? He supposed it was because her photographs had such emotional impact that he'd thought it best to approach her on that level. But he'd had enough experience with people to know that everyone had a touch of avarice in them. The question was, did Liana Stevens have enough of it that the money would change her mind?

Knowing there was only one way to find out, Sam propped his forearms on the small table and leaned toward her. "Is the money enticing enough to make you reconsider?"

Realizing her mouth was still open, Liana closed it and leaned back against her seat to place some distance between them. She turned her head to look out the window as she tried to pull herself together. She didn't want or need his money, but the amount he was willing to pay made her understand how important this project was to him. His earlier words about his grandfather came tumbling back. *All I want to do is give him something special, something that shows him how much I love him.*

If Sam Dillon had searched for a hundred years, he could have never found words that would have touched her as deeply as those had. But she'd vowed that she would never touch a camera again. Could she break that vow, even if it was for a good cause? Her mind said absolutely not, but her heart begged her to think of that old man.

She glanced back at Sam. He was still leaning halfway across the table, but his eyes were no longer shuttered. They were filled with hopeful expectancy, and she inwardly cursed him as a feeling of compassion welled up inside her. She didn't want to feel. It hurt too much, but the assertion didn't make the emotion go away.

She should have never let him into the house, she decided. She should have never offered him that second cup of coffee. She should have never... She stopped herself. All the admonitions in the world wouldn't change anything. The fact was, Sam Dillon was here and she was going to have to make a decision.

"Well?" he inquired softly.

Her heart again cried, "Yes!" But as she stared at her hands her mind provided her with a horrifying flash from the past. She was unaware of the tears glinting in her eyes as she glanced back up at Sam. "I'm sorry, Mr. Dillon, but I'm retired." With that, she rose and walked out the back door.

SAM'S FIRST IMPULSE was to go after Liana as the door slammed closed behind her. There'd been tears in her eyes. Real, honest-to-God tears. But even as he rose to his feet to follow her, some inner voice told him it would be best for him to leave.

He raked his hand through his hair as he wavered in indecision. The woman was hurting, and he'd caused the pain. But how? All he'd done was ask her to take a few rolls of pictures and offered her a hefty chunk of money to do it. As he frowned at the back door, his mind recalled that terrible look of unholy torment in her eyes. He'd never seen anything like it and he hoped he never would again.

With a sigh, he pivoted on his heel, walked through Liana Steven's strange living room and out her front door. Sam climbed into his four-wheel drive, started the engine, and then cast one last glance at Liana's home before he backed out of her drive. He wasn't done here, but he'd give her some time while he tried to figure out a way to convince her to take his pictures.

He hadn't even realized where he was heading until he stopped in front of his mother's small red-brick home. He smiled wryly as he got out of his car and headed for the door. Whenever he was confronted with a situation he wasn't sure how to handle, he always went to the one source that provided him with comfort, if not answers.

His grandfather, due to his failing health, had been forced to move in with his daughter, Sam's mother, and Sam knew the old man hated his dependency on her. However, Sam knew that he'd hate a nursing home more, and he prayed that that eventuality never came to pass. He loved the old man dearly, couldn't imagine life without him, but when the time came that he had to lose him, he wanted his grandfather to go with his dignity intact.

"Sam!" his mother, Abigail Dillon, exclaimed in surprised delight when he walked into the kitchen. "You should have let me know you were coming, and I would have cooked something special for dinner."

"I won't be staying that long," he said, automatically dropping a peck to her cheek and giving her a quick hug. "How's Gramps?"

Abigail released a heartfelt sigh and shook her head. "He's the same, and I'm worried about this depression. The doctor says it's normal after all he's been through, but I know that it isn't normal for him. He's always been able to pick himself up, no matter what he's been faced with. It scares me, Sam.''

''I know,'' Sam said, pulling her tall, still-slender body back into his arms for another hug and pressed a soothing kiss to the top of her salt-and-pepper hair. ''I'm working on something that will cheer him up. Is he in his room?''

''Yes. I haven't been able to coax him out of it. He just sits in that chair and stares out the window at the mountains.''

''Well, maybe I can coax him out.''

But when Sam knocked on his grandfather's door and opened it, he knew he was on an impossible mission. The old man never removed his gaze from the window to see who his visitor was.

''You have a great view, Gramps,'' he said as he walked to the old man and laid his hand on his shoulder. It startled him to touch his grandfather and feel his frailty. Justin Theodore Jones had always been robust and bigger than life.

''It is pretty,'' his grandfather acknowledged. ''I was just sitting here thinking about that year you went up there with me. Do you remember that year?''

''Yes,'' Sam answered as he stared at the mountains. It had been six months following his father's unexpected suicide, and Sam was now convinced that if it hadn't been for that unforgettable trip, he would have eventually followed in his father's footsteps. It was a nightmare that still haunted him.

''That trip was the most memorable event of my life, Gramps,'' he said hoarsely. ''I'll never forget it.''

When his grandfather didn't respond, but continued to gaze out the window, Sam left, quietly closing the door behind him and vowing that somehow he'd convince Liana Stevens to take his photographs. She had to, because it was the only way he could repay his grandfather for teaching him how to maintain his sanity and to get on with his life.

Chapter Two

For the past three years, Liana had welcomed the monotony of her job as manager/technician at Linden Photo Processing, a small, thriving film developing business. But during the past week, she'd discovered that the mindless chores of feeding film into a machine, filling out supply forms, and setting up the employee work schedule left her with far too many hours to think.

She felt guilty about refusing Sam Dillon's offer. Her common sense insisted that she'd had to give him an unequivocal no, yet another part of her—the human part that she'd thought long dead—argued that she shouldn't have turned her back on an old man who might never see another spring.

She was wrestling with that interminable debate when her boss and old friend, Neal Linden, came into the back room with a box of doughnuts and two foam cups filled with steaming liquid.

"Sit," Neal ordered as he placed everything on a nearby table.

"Give me a couple of minutes," Liana responded as she grabbed a roll of film, wondering why Neal was here. He was a newspaper photojournalist who'd opened this business as a sideline. Since he'd hired her, he only came to the store once a month to sign checks, and he wasn't due for another two and a half weeks. "I only have two more rolls to process, and . . ."

Neal walked over, removed the film from her hand, and led her to the table. "Sit," he said again as he pushed her into a chair.

Liana took the cup of hot tea he handed her and shook her head when he placed a chocolate-frosted doughnut on a napkin in front of her. "Neal, you know I don't eat sweets."

"Humor me," he replied as he took a healthy bite of a jelly-filled doughnut. "You know how I hate to eat alone, particularly when I'm gorging myself."

"Maybe you should become a closet gorger," Liana said as her gaze swept down his slim frame while he finished off the confection. "If you get much skinnier, you're going to be asked to pose as a famine victim."

Neal chuckled and downed a second pastry. "I have a high metabolic rate." He leaned forward, broke off a piece of a doughnut, and held it to her lips. "Indulge for once, Liana. A little sugar is good for the soul."

"And hell on the wardrobe."

His blue eyes danced merrily over her lush curves. "I pay you enough to expand your wardrobe."

She reluctantly accepted the piece of doughnut he was feeding her and mumbled around it, "So I can assume that this coffee klatch is not to tell me that I'm being fired?"

"It's a tea klatch, and no, you're not being fired, although, if I had any sense I'd do so. You don't belong in a back room processing film. You belong out in the world behind a camera."

"Neal," she warned softly.

"I know, the subject is taboo." He raked his hand through his dishwater blond hair. "If I had any sense, I'd say to hell with the taboo also, but I've always been a sucker for a good-looking, down-on-her-luck friend. Particularly one who's managed my store for the past three years with as much enthusiasm as a zombie. One good thing about you," he teased, his lips curving into a devilish grin, "you're great to have around at Halloween. It saves me money on scary decorations."

"Ha, ha," Liana muttered dryly as she absently broke off another piece of doughnut and popped it into her mouth. "Are you ready to get to the point of this so-far-inane conversation?"

He sobered so suddenly that Liana frowned in concern. Though nearly five years her senior, Neal was her closest friend. They'd met when she was in college and he'd been a guest lecturer for one of her photography classes. Each student had been asked to bring what they considered a newsworthy photograph to class, and Neal had critiqued each one. He'd been so impressed with Liana's photo of homeless people waiting in a soup line that he'd offered her a summer job as his protégeé. That summer had proved to be a major turning point in her life.

"What is it, Neal?" she asked, knowing instinctively that she wasn't going to like whatever he was going to say.

His smile was almost grim. "Well, as the old saying goes, I've got good news, and I've got bad news." He stared at her steadily as he announced, "I've just been offered a position with *The London Times*."

"That's wonderful! It's what you've always wanted." Liana gave a confused shake of her head. "So what's the bad news?"

He glanced uneasily around the room. "I have to sell this business, and I can't guarantee that I can sell you with it."

Liana felt as if the proverbial rug had just been jerked from beneath her feet. She was happy for Neal, because this was a dream he'd had for as long as she'd known him. His parents had immigrated from London when he was a child, and he'd always yearned to go back to the country of his roots. But without this job, how was she supposed to survive? All she knew was photography, and there was no way that she could get back behind a camera, not even in the tame environment of a portrait studio. Developing film had been the perfect solution.

"I don't suppose you can get your hands on enough money to buy me out," Neal said hopefully. "You'd only need about $25,000."

"*Only* need about $25,000?" she repeated. "Neal, I could barely lay my hands on $2,500. You know how I was during my misspent youth. Money burned a hole in my pocket, and what little I did manage to save over the years I had to put into my house in order to qualify for a mortgage."

"What about your parents? They're rolling in dough. Surely they'd be willing to give you a loan."

Liana closed her eyes for a moment, fighting against the stirring of emotion that Neal's question caused. She hadn't been in contact with her parents since the debacle in South America, and she'd never be able to forget the horror in their eyes when she'd told them the story of Bill's death and the part she'd had in it. Their reaction had expressed the sickening disgust she felt about herself, and she'd decided to save them the anguish of having to deal with it by never seeing them again.

"I can't ask my parents for money."

"Isn't there some way you could come up with the funds?" he persisted.

Liana parted her lips to say there was no way she could come up with the money, but Sam Dillon's outrageous offer surfaced. She had considered accepting his job on a purely philanthropic basis. Could she consider it on a selfish one? If she combined what he was offering with her minimal savings, she might be able to swing a loan.

Her sense of decency said she couldn't possibly consider taking Sam's job, but if she lost her job here, how would she survive? If she took this one assignment she'd be able to buy Neal's store, and then she'd be assured that she'd never have to touch a camera again. But could she do it? Was she physically capable of actually holding a camera in her hands? Of focusing it and pushing down the shutter button? There was only one way to find out, but was she strong enough to test herself?

"There might be one way," she said hesitantly, "but I'd have to cut my hours here, which means you'd have to work here part-time."

"Honey, I'll do everything I can to make it easy for you," Neal said, reaching over to pat her hand solicitously. "Or at least I will for as long as I can. I have to be in London in eight weeks, which means I have to put the business on the market within the month."

LIANA STOOD OUTSIDE the small Mexican restaurant where she'd asked Sam to meet her and transferred her purse from one shoulder to the other. Could she really walk in there and accept his job? And what if she did and discovered that she was incapable of taking his pictures? Not only would she let him down, but she'd lose any chance she had at buying Neal's business. Her palms were damp and she rubbed them against her brown linen pants legs as she tried to decide whether to stay or to run.

"Oh, good, I haven't kept you waiting," Sam announced as he walked up beside her, took her elbow and steered her toward the restaurant's door. "I'm afraid my last appointment ran later than it should have." He smiled at her as he pushed open the door and ushered her inside. "Even my secretary couldn't scare the man off."

"What business are you in?" Liana inquired, suddenly realizing that she knew absolutely nothing about this man but his name, that his grandfather was ill, and that he was willing to pay her a small fortune to take his pictures.

"Roofing," Sam answered, then informed the hostess, "two in nonsmoking." He glanced toward Liana quickly, one brow arched in question. "You don't smoke, do you?"

"No."

They were silent as they followed the woman to their table, and Liana mulled over his occupation. It explained his well-muscled physique, and she had no doubt that he could be found working with a hammer in his hand more often than behind an office desk. The leashed tension that radiated from him would demand a physical outlet.

After they were seated, Sam asked, "Have you eaten here before?"

"Several times," she answered, her voice husky with nervous tension as his green eyes treated her to a slow, analytical appraisal that gave her the oddest feeling that he was probing her mind. The sensation caused a delicate shiver of anxiety to race up her spine.

He set his menu aside. "In that case, I'll let you order for me."

"Okay," she agreed, relieved to be able to redirect her attention to the menu. "Do you like things hot?"

She regretted the question the moment it popped out of her mouth and she risked a glance toward Sam, chagrined to see his lips lift in a suggestive smile. She could feel the color flooding her cheeks and blessed the fact that they were sitting in a dark corner so the blush wouldn't be noticeable.

Sam knew he shouldn't tease her, but the line was too perfect to pass up, particularly when he could see that Liana was rattled by her inadvertent slip of the tongue. He'd also swear that she was blushing, which he found fascinating. It appeared that her shell was easier to penetrate than he'd imagined.

"When it comes to food, no," he said in a purposely seductive drawl, curious to see how she'd react.

"Mild?" she asked, refusing to acknowledge his innuendo. He was staring at her, but his eyes were hooded, which made her even more nervous.

"When it comes to food, yes," he said, convinced that she was blushing when the color in her cheeks deepened. He felt inordinately pleased at having been able to fluster her.

"We could have eaten somewhere else if you don't like Mexican food."

"I like Mexican food."

Liana nodded and laid the menu aside. When Sam's gaze centered on her hands, she realized that her fingers were knotted together. She slowly pulled them apart and slipped her hands into her lap.

She re-knotted her fingers as she looked at Sam. He'd been handsome when he'd visited her home, but in his three-piece charcoal-gray suit and pale yellow shirt he took the term into another dimension. Oddly enough, the suit also made him look more intimidating. She wondered how in the world she was going to approach him about his job offer, and what would she do if he'd already hired someone else?

She waited, hoping he'd bring up the subject, and when he didn't, she found herself struggling for the courage to do so. To her immense relief, the waitress chose that moment to approach their table, giving her a much needed delay to pull herself together.

While Liana ordered for them, Sam studied her thoughtfully. He'd been shocked when she'd called and invited him to lunch. When she'd turned down his offer of money and walked out on him, he'd been sure that he'd have to come up with some wild scheme to get her to take his pictures. Now he wondered if she'd pulled that melodramatic stunt in order to up the ante.

"I was surprised to receive your call. Does this mean you're going to take my pictures?" Sam asked when the waitress left.

Liana was flooded with relief. He hadn't hired someone else. She gazed at an unseen point over his shoulder. "I'm thinking about it. Were you serious about the payment you quoted?"

"Yes," Sam answered, and Liana felt the sudden tension in him.

She glanced at him, only to discover that his eyes were still hooded, watchful. "It's an outrageous amount of money."

He ran a finger along his bottom lip and tilted his head as he regarded her. She hated the fact that she couldn't see his eyes, and she mentally cursed the linen napkin in her lap that couldn't be shredded.

"My grandfather is worth it," he finally said.

"I wasn't implying that he wasn't." When Sam didn't respond, she transferred her gaze back to that unseen spot. "How much time do you think the project will take?"

Sam, who'd been waiting for her to raise the price and knew this was the perfect point for her to do so, leaned back and laced his fingers behind his head. His languid pose belied the terse tone in his voice. "I suppose that depends on how much more money you're going to charge me."

Liana's gaze flew to him in confusion. "How much more money I'm going to charge you?"

His hands came from behind his head and his forearms landed on the table. "Isn't that what this meeting is all about? I made you an outrageous offer, and now you're coming back with an even more outrageous counteroffer?"

There was a distinct curl to his upper lip as he stated tightly, "I'm not in the mood for playing a negotiating game. Just tell me what you want, and I'll meet your price, but you'd better make damn sure that every photograph you take is worth it."

It had been so long since Liana had felt anything as elemental as anger that at first she didn't recognize the emotion. When she did, she drew in a deep breath and let righteous indignation flow through her. She'd come here prepared to take the job, even if it did go against every moral fiber of her being, and he was accusing her of trying to swindle him!

She snatched up her purse, withdrew a handful of bills and tossed them carelessly on top of the table. "Lunch is on me," she said in a low whisper that was filled with fury, "and you can take your outrageous offer and..."

The waitress chose that moment to arrive. "Watch the plates. They're hot," she informed them cheerfully.

That wasn't all that was hot, Sam thought. Liana's eyes were positively sizzling, and he wondered why his suit wasn't smoking beneath their angry gaze. *This* was the woman who had won awards and acclaims. He'd known instinctively that her feelings would run deeper, be far more intense, than the average person's. How else could she have become a master of capturing emotion on film at such a young age?

Certain that Liana would bolt the moment the waitress was out of the way, he reached across the table and grasped her wrist. She winced at his grip, and he loosened it slightly, even though he knew he wasn't hurting her.

"Let me go," she demanded the moment the waitress had walked away.

"No," he said quietly but firmly. "I've insulted you, and I'm sorry. The only defense I can offer for myself is that I've been at the using end of life far too often not to be suspicious. I want you to take my pictures, Liana, and if it will soothe your maligned dignity, I'll even lower my outrageous offer.''

"Lower it?" Linda repeated weakly, forgetting her anger as she saw Linden Photo Processing flying right out the window.

Sam narrowed his eyes as he realized it was the money that had brought her here. Intuition told him she needed it badly. He wanted to ask her what she needed it for, but he knew he was on tenuous ground.

Instead, he said, "I'll lower it by one dollar."

Her relief was evident in her sudden sagging posture and the rapid, fluttering pulse that beat beneath his fingertips. He found himself wanting to caress the delicate skin stretched over her pulse until it calmed, and he had to force himself to release her wrist.

He watched in fascination as the spark of life began to drain from her eyes, returning them to that cold, empty state, and he wondered if she did it consciously or if it had become a subconscious habit. He had a feeling it was the latter.

"What?" he murmured absently, realizing she'd been speaking and he hadn't been listening.

"How much time do you think this project will take?"

"About a month. Most of the areas my grandfather's frequented we can hit in daily jaunts if we leave early in the morning. But there is one area we'll have to hike to. I figure two days in and two days out."

"Would we be able to begin immediately?"

Sam hesitated as his mind flew over the roofing contracts that were in progress or very near starting dates, two of which were on new malls. He'd figured on at least a week to get his affairs in order, but he knew his foreman, Pat Williams, could handle whatever was on the docket, and if

Liana was willing to take the pictures, he wasn't going quibble over time.

"I can begin tomorrow."

Liana shook her head. "I need a few days to get prepared. Is Saturday all right?"

"Saturday," he agreed.

LIANA STOOD IN THE CENTER of her basement and looked at the carefully lettered, neatly stacked boxes that represented the first twenty-nine years of her life. To her surprise, it wasn't the listing of contents that disturbed her as much as the orderliness of the boxes, which were lined in perfect symmetry against the wall.

Until she'd moved into this house, she'd been a pack rat who'd believed that everything had its place and it was wherever you dropped it. She'd come to the conclusion that that philosophy had been a reflection of her inability to face life. By cluttering her world with the nonsensical and the nonessential, she hadn't had to acknowledge the stark reality surrounding her.

Unfortunately, while she indulged herself in her folly, life had patiently waited for her to lull herself into a sense of complacency. Then, when she had least expected it, it had ripped away all the trappings and forced her to come face-to-face with that reality.

She had to place both hands against a wooden beam to handle the wave of pain that swept through her as she recalled how harshly she'd been taught that lesson. With the pain came remorse, guilt, and a thousand other related feelings that she couldn't even define as images of Bill danced through her mind.

Heaven help her, she didn't want to feel! But no matter how hard she tried, she couldn't hold back the flood of emotions that had been dormant for so long that they were as tender as a festering wound.

She rested her forehead against the wood and cursed Sam Dillon. He'd walked uninvited into her life and punched a hole through her carefully erected barriers. If she had any sense at all, she'd go upstairs, call him and tell him she'd changed her mind.

But, she reminded herself, she needed this job. Without it she couldn't buy Neal's business, and if she didn't buy it, she wouldn't have a secure future. Only by being her own boss would she be guaranteed control over her life, specifically the freedom of never again having to touch a camera.

She drew in a deep breath and exhaled slowly, forcing her emotions back into check. But even as she walked to the boxes with that familiar feeling of detachment, deep inside she knew that she'd only managed to put a precarious patch over the hole Sam had put in her self-protective walls. If she went through with this project, there was every possibility that he would do even more damage, because Sam had a knack of making her react.

When she found herself absently stroking the wrist he'd held that afternoon, she again told herself to go upstairs, call him and cancel before it was too late. Instead, she removed the box labeled photography equipment from the pile and tore open the lid.

IT WAS NEARLY MIDNIGHT, but Sam was too wound up to sleep. He sat on a chair in front of his bedroom window, his bare feet resting on the sill as he stared out into the moonless night.

Without even knowing how he'd done it, he'd accomplished what he'd set out to do. Tomorrow, Liana Stevens would begin taking his pictures. However, Sam couldn't help but wonder what price she was going to pay by doing so, and he had no doubt that the expedition was going to cost her. The terrible torment he'd seen in her eyes that first day haunted him, and no matter how much he told himself to ignore it, he couldn't.

As his grandfather would say, it was evident that Liana was going through a severe emotional winter. Would taking her into the mountains, as his grandfather had done with him, help her weather that season and allow her to look forward to better times or would it make her draw her cloak of despair more tightly around her?

Sam was torn by the questions, and he wondered if he shouldn't do as she'd suggested in her letters and telephone conversations with him, which was look for another photographer. But he wanted to gift his grandfather with the best, and he was convinced that only Liana could guarantee that.

On its own accord, his mind conjured up the image of her as she'd been in the restaurant a few days before, her eyes flashing with anger, her cheeks flushed and her breasts heaving. His fingers tingled in memory of the soft delicate flesh on the underside of her wrist and her fluttering pulse, which had been beating in the wild cadence of a captured bird.

Several words flowed through his mind, describing what he felt for her. Attraction, fascination and curiosity were at the top of the list, and he analyzed each of the emotions in turn.

The attraction was easily understood. Physically, she was one of the most beautiful women he'd ever seen. He'd have to be dead not to respond to her. The fascination was a bit more complicated, because he normally shied away from people with problems. He had enough of his own to cope with, and he certainly didn't need to load himself down with someone else's troubles. He supposed it was his curiosity that made her the exception to that rule. What could have possibly happened that would make her withdraw so completely from life?

As he continued to stare out the window, Sam gave his imagination full rein, but he couldn't create one scenario horrific enough to explain the mystery of Liana. To his chagrin, the exercise only made him more fascinated with her. He supposed he could go to his old high school friend, Neal Linden, who'd referred him to Liana in the first place to get some answers, but for some reason he found that solution untenable. He wanted to know about her, but he didn't want the information to come second hand. He wanted to learn about Liana from Liana, and that need was the most fascinating of all to him.

He glanced toward the illuminated dial of his clock. The late hour convinced him he had to get some sleep, and he rose to his feet and stretched. In less than six hours he'd be picking up Liana, and with any luck, by this time tomorrow he'd begin to get some answers to all his puzzling questions.

Chapter Three

When Sam pulled his four-wheel drive to a stop in Liana's driveway, the sun was poking its way over the horizon. He glanced toward it, narrowing his eyes against the blinding slice of brilliant vermilion.

He was pleased to note that there wasn't a cloud in sight, which upheld the weatherman's prediction of good weather. Though it hadn't snowed in a month, Sam knew it wouldn't be unusual to have a late spring snowfall, particularly in the high mountains.

He walked to Liana's front door and rang the bell. As he waited, he turned to watch the sun creep higher into the sky. The reddish orb was lightening to a burnt orange with a halo of gold and even when he heard the door open, he was unable to tear his gaze away from its magnificent beauty.

Liana involuntarily caught her breath when her gaze landed on Sam. The rising sun lit his profile and she widened her eyes in appreciation. His dark hair glistened and the silver in it shimmered like elusive veins of precious metal. The sharp length of his nose, the lean hollow of his cheek, and the jutting of his chin should have made him look harsh. But his features were softened by the silken length of lashes that half shielded his eyes and cast a feathery shadow along the high ridge of his cheekbone.

It took an effort to pull her eyes away from his face, and she had to force herself to release her breath as they glided down his body. He was dressed as casually as the first time he'd come to see her, except his chambray shirt had been replaced by a blue-and black-checked wool one and he wore a red down vest instead of the denim jacket. His jeans hung low on his hips, embracing his flat abdomen, curving over the swell of his taut buttocks and clinging to his muscular thighs. She once again found her shutter-button finger itching to capture him on film, and she was as bewildered by the impulse now as she had been the first time.

When she returned her gaze to his face, she found him watching her, one half of his face cast in light and the other in shadow. That contrast made it impossible for her to read his expression. She automatically moved back, feeling threatened, though she didn't know if she perceived the threat as coming from him or from within herself.

Sam, sensing her sudden wariness, forced himself into an easy stance with his hands still tucked into his back pockets, although he was far from feeling relaxed. When he'd finally glanced away from the sun, he'd been surprised to find Liana studying him. He'd also been chagrined when he'd felt desire stir beneath her feminine scrutiny.

And why not? he asked himself ruefully as he let his gaze flick over her in a swift appraisal. She was beautiful.

She'd braided her inordinately long hair and twisted it into a loose knot at the back of her neck. The sleek coiffure emphasized the classic lines of her face and made her eyes appear enormous. He was relieved to see that they no longer looked empty but remote. Like him, she wore a wool shirt, denims and hiking boots, and looked as alluring as he imagined she would in a flowing silk dress.

In an effort to divert his attention, he glanced over her shoulder to see a day pack leaning against the wall with a light blue parka draped over it.

"Good morning, Liana. Are you ready to go?"

Liana nodded and reached for her parka. As she pulled it on, Sam stepped inside and lifted her pack. While she locked the door, he carried the pack out to the four-wheel drive. By the time he'd stored it in the back, Liana was climbing into the passenger seat.

He joined her, twisted the ignition key, and said, "We'll be stopping at a friend's ranch that's near one of the trails my grandfather used. He's agreed to loan us a couple of his horses if you'd prefer to ride instead of hike."

Liana stared straight ahead, far too aware of Sam and his innate masculinity to risk glancing at him. She told herself that if she had one ounce of common sense, she'd go back into her house and lock the door behind her. Her fingers twitched at the suggestion, but she didn't reach for the door handle.

"Actually, I'd prefer to hike," she replied. "That way we won't disturb the wildlife and I'll be able to get more and better pictures."

"If that's what you prefer, then that's what we'll do."

A tense silence fell between them. When Sam pulled onto the Interstate, Liana peered out the side window, watching the sprawling metropolis of Denver and its surrounding communities disappear, replaced by wooded mountains, with occasional glimpses of small country towns as they left the highway and traveled mountain roads. Eventually she began to relax, lulled by the hum of tires on the pavement and the hypnotic flash of evergreen tree after evergreen tree. Nearly two hours had passed when Sam suddenly pulled into the parking lot of a roadside café, and Liana glanced toward him in confusion.

Sam's hands tightened reflexively around the steering wheel as he stared at her face. She looked like a startled doe, uncertain as to whether she faced safety or danger.

He lowered his voice to an octave he'd use to calm a skittish horse. "I didn't have breakfast, and I'm hungry. If I don't eat, my stomach will be growling all morning, and I can guarantee that it will scare away every living creature within a five-mile radius."

"Oh," Liana whispered. His eyes were alight with self-deprecating humor, and his smile was easy and friendly. He didn't look threatening, but she still felt threatened. She told herself she was being melodramatic. The assertion helped— at least a little. "Then I guess we'd better feed you."

A moment later Sam opened the door to the small café and waited for her to precede him. Liana's eyes swept over the room that was inelegant but sparkling clean. The matronly waitress behind the counter smiled and told them to take a seat. Liana slid into the nearest booth.

Sam sat across from her, reached for the single page, hand-typed menus and dropped one in front of her.

Liana lifted the menu and studied it with feigned interest, her nerves too tightly strung for her stomach to digest food. She still wasn't convinced that she could take Sam's pictures, and she cast a glance at him. He was looking at her, his lips curved in a friendly smile.

"I just realized that I never said thank you for taking this job," he told her. "It means a lot to me."

"You're paying me to do it," she reminded him.

There was a momentary flare of anger in his eyes, but it immediately disappeared. "Yes, but there's nothing wrong with one business associate thanking another for their services, is there?"

"No," Liana responded, albeit reluctantly, because she wondered if he'd still be thanking her by the end of the day.

She returned her attention to the menu as the waitress arrived to take her order, deciding that she could force down some toast and a soft-boiled egg.

When the woman set their plates in front of them a short time later, Liana watched Sam dig into his ham and eggs and country fries with the exuberance of a starving man. She arched a brow as she said, "You really were hungry."

Sam glanced up at her in shocked surprise. It was the first time she'd initiated any form of conversation with him, and he'd been wondering if he was destined to spend the next month incommunicado.

"It's all that fresh air. Besides, I never have more than a bowl of cereal for breakfast, so whenever I get the opportunity to load up on cholesterol, I do it with gusto."

Liana actually felt the corners of her lips twitch at his artless confession, which only reminded her how dangerous he was. She returned her attention to her plate.

Sam bit back a sigh as he watched her withdraw from him. He searched his mind for some topic of conversation he could introduce to get her talking again. Unfortunately, the only one he could come up with was the weather, and he decided that was too obvious a ploy.

He was still sipping his coffee when Liana pushed away her plate and asked, "Are you married?"

"Divorced." He grimaced at the brusque tone of his voice. After two years it shouldn't still hurt, but it did.

"I'm sorry. I didn't mean to pry."

Sam watched contriteness flare into her eyes, and the word "enigma" once again raced through his mind. How could she look so detached one minute, and so human the next?

"You weren't prying. It's just that my toes are still a little sore from being stepped on. For fifteen years, while I was building my small—and I emphasize small—fortune, my wife was quite content to spend it in an effort to climb the social ladder. Then, a couple of years ago she decided that me and my profession weren't good enough for her social status. She packed her bags and walked out. I got my divorce papers one day, and she married a high-powered attorney the next."

Liana's heart went out to him as she watched the emotions flicker across his face. He was trying to look cavalier, but she could see the pain in his eyes. She couldn't help but wonder what kind of foolish woman would turn her back on a man like Sam Dillon. Not only was he handsome, but he'd spent an entire month badgering her about taking his grandfather's pictures, refusing to take no for an answer. She knew instinctively that he would do the same for a wife. That kind of love and devotion should be savored and treasured, not cast aside for social prominence.

Needing to erase the pain she'd inadertently caused him, she said, "My great-grandfather started building my family's fortune by opening a trash collection business in New York City. After he was gone and my grandfather took over, my grandmother decided that she didn't want to be known as the queen of trash. She convinced him to sell out and they went into garbage of another kind."

Sam waited for her to deliver the punch line, and when she only took a sip of her tea, he grinned and said, "Okay, I'll bite. What kind of garbage did they go into?"

She leaned toward him, lowered her voice to a conspiratorial whisper, and deadpanned, "Fast food."

It was her delivery, more than her announcement, that made Sam burst into laughter. "Lady, I think I like you."

His words were so direct and uncomplicated that Liana was serious when she said, "I think I like you too, Sam Dillon." *And that scares the hell out of me*, she added silently. Before he could respond, she continued, "I think it's time we get to work on those photographs for your grand-father.''

Sam knew she was deliberately ending the moment of ca-maraderie. He also understood that that sense of unity had disturbed her. He wanted to reach across the table, shake her, and demand that she tell him why she was so fright-ened, because he also knew that it was fear that made those beautiful eyes so empty.

Instead, he picked up the bill and walked to the cash reg-ister. While he paid it, Liana went out to the car. When he joined her, she was once again staring out the window, but Sam was willing to accept her isolation, for he was con-vinced that it was all a facade. He decided that during the next few weeks it was going to be interesting to watch the hidden facets of Liana Stevens reveal themselves.

THEY ARRIVED at Sam's friend's ranch, and Sam left Liana by the car while he went to tell the man they wouldn't need the horses. By the time he returned, she'd put on her day pack and slung her camera around her neck.

Since the camera had been a subconscious burden for three long years, Liana had expected it to feel like a mill-stone. She was, therefore, surprised at how easily she ad-justed to its weight.

When Sam pointed out the trail they'd be taking, Liana forged ahead while he slipped on his pack. She knew the exact moment when Sam caught up with her, though he moved silently behind her. They didn't speak as they hiked into the wilderness, and Liana's eyes were in constant mo-tion.

Since her last memories of South America were of soar-ing mountain peaks, she didn't look at the ones facing her now. Instead, she concentrated on her immediate sur-roundings, telling herself to adapt to the environment a piece at a time to discover the subtle differences between the Rockies and the Andes.

She drew in a deep breath, savoring the cool, crisp air that was in counterpoint to the memory of heavy, oppressive air. Instead of lush tropical growth, the ground here was sparse with vegetation. There were patches of snow buried in shadow, and fragile green spouts were bravely poking their way out of the ground. Even the trees were different, more stark and misshapen, the result of a harsher climate.

The sounds were different, too. There was wind here, and it sighed as it blew, rustling the burgeoning leaves of aspens and scrub oaks. The animals were more subdued, less restive and less vociferous, and she didn't hear one insect. That fact relaxed her. God, how she'd hated the insects.

The higher they climbed, the more relaxed Liana became, the more aware of everything around her, and when they walked into a clearing of soft, rolling green that was filled with early blooming wild flowers, whose colors ranged from white to yellow to red, with even a spot or two of purple, she caught her breath in wonder. But no matter how hard she tried, she couldn't force herself to lift the camera and capture the scene on film.

She had no idea how much time had passed before her body told her it was time to take a break, and she dropped down on a large stone at the side of the trail and lifted her canteen to her mouth. Sam dropped to one knee beside her and mimicked her action. They studied each other, both silently assuring themselves that the other was physically capable of moving on. Liana decided that there really was a silver lining in every black cloud. Her nightmarish nights had sent her prowling the streets every morning, and her body was more fit than it had ever been.

At noon, Sam caught her arm, cast a significant glance at his watch, and removed a pack of beef jerky from his vest pocket. When he ripped off the top and extended it toward her, Liana took two pieces and gnawed on them as she sat down on another rock that overlooked a canyon. Again, Sam sat beside her, and they gazed down at the peaceful valley below them.

It was only when Sam slipped off his pack and retrieved two bags of trail mix from it that Liana felt a need to break the silence. As she took the offered food, she said, "I'm sorry I haven't taken any photographs."

Sam shrugged dismissively, his gaze still centered on the valley. "When you see something that sparks your imagination, you'll take a ton of pictures."

Liana wished she could be as sure of that statement as he sounded. She may have adjusted to the weight of the camera around her neck, but, as she'd already discovered, she simply hadn't been able to lift it into her hands. Had she led both herself and Sam on a wild goose chase?

Sam appeared to read her thoughts. He glanced toward her and said, "When it's right, Liana, you'll know it."

She leaned her elbows on her knees and said, "Why don't you tell me about your grandfather and his trips into the mountains? Having some insight into him might give me a better idea of what we're looking for."

"That sounds like a good idea."

Sam picked up a handful of small stones and tossed them over the cliff one by one, while trying to figure out how he could convey the essence of his grandfather in words.

Eventually, he said, "When I was five or six years old, my mother told me the story of Paul Bunyan. As I listened to her, I closed my eyes and conjured up the image of my grandfather. He was a massive man, and to a kid, he was big enough to be a giant. The next time I saw him, I told him that I thought he was Paul Bunyan. He just laughed and said that as I grew up, I'd scale him down to size."

He paused as he gathered up another handful of stones and began to toss them after the others. "He was right. As I grew, I realized that although he was larger than most men, he wasn't a giant. However, in my heart, he was still Paul Bunyan. It was a long time before I recognized that I felt that way because he was a giant on the inside."

"You idolized him," Liana murmured, knowing the observation was apparent, but feeling as if she needed to say something.

"Yeah," Sam answered. "I still do. He has more goodness in his little finger than most people have in their entire body."

He braced his foot on the rock, linked his arm around his leg, and rested his chin on his knee. "He's the only person I've ever met who can cut through the chase and get right to the heart of a matter. Where anyone else would sit around stewing or wallowing in self-pity over a problem, he indentifies it and comes up with a solution. It might not always be the right solution, but it's a solution.

"One day I asked him how he managed to just tackle life head on, and he said, 'Son, every year of a man's life has its emotional seasons. We have our months of spring where everything is new and exciting. Then we have our months of summer where everything is calm. We have our fickle falls where our lives sway up and down, and we have our winters when our days are the bleakest. I've learned to cope with my winters by going to the mountains every spring to watch life renew and perpetuate itself. It reminds me that I have to throw off my cloak of despair in order to live again, and our time on this earth is just too damn short to spend it all in winter.' Then he told me to find something in my life that would make me look forward to spring and I'd be able to handle anything life throws at me."

"Did you ever come up here with him?" Liana asked when he once again fell into silence.

Sam hesitated a moment before saying, "He brought me up here when I was sixteen. It was six months after my father's death, and I hadn't been able to cope with it. Gramps thought the trip would help me regain my perspective, and he was right."

Liana watched a shadowed look flicker across his face, and she knew that she'd once again inadvertently touched on a tender subject. She wanted to ask him how his father had died, but intuition told her she should leave the matter alone.

Instead, she said, "You haven't told me what's wrong with your grandfather. Do you mind discussing it?"

Again, he hesitated, but then said, "He had a small stroke at the beginning of the year, and it was followed by a massive heart attack. He's recovered from the stroke, but he needs bypass surgery. Unfortunately, his health is too fragile to withstand the operation, so all we can do is stand by and wait for the inevitable."

The sadness in his voice caused an unexpected surge of tears to sting Liana's eyes, and she closed them, forcing the moisture to recede. Sam was making her feel, and she couldn't afford to do that. To save her remaining sanity, she had to stay detached from life. She shouldn't take another step forward with him. She should turn around and head back to Denver.

But she knew that she wouldn't—couldn't—do that. Sam had just introduced her to an old man who deserved one last spring, and she not only wanted to give it to him, she wanted to make it the best one he'd ever had.

The decision gave her the impetus to push herself to her feet and dust off the back of her jeans. "Let's go find us a view so spectacular that when your grandfather sees it, it'll knock his socks off," she stated determinedly.

Sam, startled by her words said, "Okay, but I think it will be hard to find something that spectacular. Remember, he's spent sixty-two springs in these mountains."

"Yes, but I bet he's never seen the same view twice, and he's never seen one through my eyes."

Sam didn't bother to reply because his gaze was locked on Liana's swaying posterior as she started up the trail. What she did to a pair of jeans was downright erotic, and he knew that for his own comfort he should find himself another view. Yet, no matter how hard he tried, nothing else held his interest. He finally decided that a little discomfort was a good character builder and let his eyes wander back to that delectable view.

He was so intent on watching her that he almost ran into her when she came to an abrupt halt. He frowned as he raised his eyes and peered over the top of her head, only to catch his breath at the sight in front of them.

It was late morning, but the mountain ahead was so high that the sun was just now cresting its peak, its color that same spectacular vermilion that he'd seen when he'd stood on Liana's front porch.

He shook his head, whispering, "I've never seen anything so beautiful."

When Liana didn't answer, he moved to her side so he could see her face, and everything inside him twisted into a hard, cold knot. She was deathly pale and gasping for breath.

"Liana," he said as he reached to touch her.

She jerked away from his hand. "I—I'm okay. I just need a few minutes alone."

Before Sam could answer, she walked off the trail and into the woods. The knot inside him tightened as she disappeared from sight.

Should he follow her or wait? he wondered. A part of him said he had to honor her request for privacy. A more insistent part said he had to go after her. He found himself wavering in indecision, but it didn't last long. He'd brought her up here, and he was responsible for her. She was upset, and he wasn't going to leave her alone.

Sam's concern escalated when he came to a break in the trees and saw Liana standing on the edge of a cliff. Even from the fifty feet separating them, he could see that she was trembling uncontrollably. What in the world was wrong with her? He couldn't decide whether to go to her or wait and see what happened. He decided to wait.

Unaware of Sam's presence, Liana stared at the sun easing its way from behind the mountain peak. She needed to take a picture of this for the old man, she told herself, but she couldn't touch the camera. Her palms were sweaty and her teeth were chattering, but her chill wasn't due to the cool mountain air that blew over her. Blood-red, the sun made the snow it touched appear to bleed, causing her mind to flash images of the last time she'd held this camera in her hands. That day, the blood had been real.

Her body shook so vehemently from the memories that she had to sit down. Pulling her knees up to her chest, she buried her face against them. Sam wanted to give his grandfather the beauty of spring in the Rockies, but she couldn't lift her camera, and even if she could, she'd be seeing horror, not beauty. She had to go back and tell him that she was wasting his time, that he had to hire another photographer.

But as her mind insisted she was right, her heart rebelled, sending a surge of anger flowing through her at her self-pity.

She'd made a business deal with Sam, and she was going to carry it out if it killed her. She inhaled and exhaled several times before she found the courage to raise her head.

Nearly topping the peak, the sun was now more orange than red. The words, "purple mountain majesties," came to mind as she took note of the towering pillars of rock, which had taken on a deep plum hue where the snow had already melted away. The rays of the sun colored the remaining blanket of snow from a warm gold to a blushing pink, and she watched a bald eagle take flight, seeming to fly toward the golden orb in welcome.

The images of horror still flickered through her mind, but she forced herself to concentrate on the sight before her, asking herself what a man who'd watched this same scene for sixty-two years would see. What would be familiar? What would be different? What would make his breath catch and bring tears to his eyes?

She shifted to her knees and sat back on her heels. Her hands trembled, but she lifted the camera to her face. She peered through the view finder and began to repeat those questions as she focused her lens. Her heart pounded in her chest, and her throat felt dry and raw. Panic curled in the pit of her stomach, but even fear couldn't dim the beauty as she found the eagle and framed him against the sun.

The first click of the shutter button and the whirring of the film as it automatically advanced made her flinch, but she refocused on the mountain, framing its peak which was backlighted with a magnificent blue sky, yet the heart of it was still cast in alternating patterns of light and shadow. She shot again, refocused, and then repeated the procedure over and over. Only when the roll of film was used did she allow herself to drop the camera, to lean her head back and peer up at the clear blue sky overhead. She felt drained, but she'd done it.

Several minutes passed before she found the strength to reload the camera and rise to her feet. As she walked back toward the trail, she found herself filled with a feeling of weary accomplishment.

THE MOMENT LIANA turned toward the trees, Sam headed for the trail. Some of his tension had been released when she'd taken the pictures but a part of it still lingered. However, it, too, disappeared when Liana joined him on the trail. She looked as limp as a dishrag, but there was a serenity in her face that hadn't been there before, and one of her long-fingered hands was cradling the base of her camera in a protective gesture. His remaining tension drained away as a deep inner voice assured him that everything was going to be all right.

"Everything okay?" he asked with forced affability.

Liana blushed and looked down at her feet as she realized what a fool she must have seemed when she'd taken off into the trees like a scared rabbit.

"Everything's fine. I wanted to get a more unobstructed view of that mountain so I could take some pictures."

Instinctively understanding that taking those pictures had depleted her energy, he nodded and looked up at the sky. "Some clouds are starting to move in. They don't look threatening, but I don't trust the weather this time of year. If you don't mind, I'd like to head back. We're not equipped to be caught in a sudden spring snowstorm."

Liana gratefully nodded. Taking her pictures had exhausted her, and she could think of nothing better than going home and climbing into bed. She led the way back down the trail, stopping periodically and forcing herself to take a picture of a view they'd passed earlier. The camera still felt foreign in her hands, and the panic still curled in her stomach every time she touched it, but each shot she took required a little less effort.

By the time they reached his car, she could barely lift her feet. After giving Sam her day pack, she got in, fastened her seat belt, and leaned her head against the door. When Sam climbed in beside her a short time later, she'd already fallen asleep.

A wellspring of indefinable feelings flowed through Sam as he stared at her beautiful face relaxed in sleep, and it took every bit of his self-control to keep from reaching and brushing stray strands of hair away from her cheek.

As he stared at her, he concluded that attraction, fascination and curiosity were a powerful combination. Gut instinct warned that they were also a very dangerous combination. Any man who ignored that warning was only asking for trouble, and Sam had long ago learned to avoid trouble.

He'd hired Liana to do a job, he reminded himself as he started the engine. In a few weeks that job would be over and they'd go their separate ways. The chances of him ever seeing her again were slim to none.

That last thought caused a strange little pang in the center of his chest.

LIANA WOKE just as Sam pulled off the Interstate, and she blinked at him in sleepy confusion. "We're home?"

"Just about," he answered, casting her a quick glance before returning his attention to the road, pleased to see that she looked recovered from her ordeal.

"Sorry I fell asleep like that."

"No problem."

Liana felt as if she should say something more, but she didn't know what, so she remained silent as Sam wound his way through the streets leading to her house.

When he pulled into her driveway and turned off the ignition, she started to tell him he didn't need to get out. But then she remembered that her pack was in the back and he'd have to get it for her.

She joined him while he retrieved it, and when he handed it to her, she said, "Thanks. I'll see you in the morning."

But before she could walk away, Sam caught her arm. "I always walk a lady to the door."

One look at his face convinced Liana a refusal of his gallantry would go unheeded, so she didn't even offer a protest as he accompanied her.

When they reached her door, she turned to face him and he reached out and touched her hair, murmuring, "You have pine needles in your hair."

Liana was caught so off-guard by the action, that she stood frozen in place. As he brushed the needles away, she gazed up at him, and found herself thinking that he had the type of rugged good looks that many a movie star would envy. But it was his expressive eyes that made him truly handsome, she decided. They mirrored his every mood and every thought, and what she saw reflected in their depths at this very moment made her catch her breath. He was going to kiss her.

Warmth suffused her body, but it wasn't caused by desire as much as the need to be cradled in his arms. She'd been so lost for so long that she craved the security she knew she'd find in his embrace, the tenderness she was sure she'd find in his kiss.

But even as her body began to sway toward him she also knew she couldn't accept what he was offering, because she would be taking, not giving, and Sam Dillon deserved more than that.

As Sam's hand cupped her cheek and his head lowered, Liana called upon every ounce of her willpower and took a quick step back. The look of confusion in his eyes made her glance guiltily toward the ground. "Good night, Sam." With that, she turned on her heel and walked through her front door.

Sam didn't move until the door closed behind her. Only then did he let his feelings surface, and he didn't like what they revealed. When he'd thought he was going to kiss Liana, his body had responded with the eagerness of a teenager in his prime and was still trembling. Oddly enough, it wasn't lovemaking that had been foremost in his mind but the need to erase the loneliness and sadness he sensed within her. For an instant, he'd actually felt that if he gave of himself he'd make her whole again, and that realization made him furious.

As he strode back to the car and got in, he told himself that he didn't care if Liana looked like some tragic heroine out of a Gothic novel. He didn't care if hopelessness radiated from her in waves. He didn't care if she'd chosen to bury herself in that mausoleum she called a house. He didn't care, but he was damnably intrigued.

He was becoming obsessed with her, he decided as he drove toward home, and he wasn't going to let that happen. He'd been obsessed with his wife right up to the day she'd walked out on him. Not obsessed in a manic way, of course, he assured himself. He hadn't been jealous or possessive; he'd simply been driven to give her everything that would make her happy.

He frowned at that admission. Had he been trying to buy Kay's love? He tried to deny the question but couldn't, and as he let his mind travel over those fifteen years of marriage, he realized how often he'd subjugated his own needs so that Kay could have her way. He'd even convinced himself that he didn't want a family because Kay hadn't wanted one.

Yes, he'd been obsessed, and he'd been a fool. He'd wasted fifteen years of his life on a selfish, shallow woman. To make matters worse, he knew that if she hadn't walked out on him, he'd probably still be playing the game. He'd only been nineteen when they'd married, but he'd taken his marriage vows seriously and had had every intention of upholding them for life.

He muttered an oath when he realized that tonight, he'd almost ended up making an even bigger fool of himself with Liana, and he had to remind himself that he'd hired her to do a job. Nothing more and nothing less. So what if she did have problems? He wasn't some quixotic knight in shining armor who raced around rescuing damsels in distress. He was a sensible man with both feet planted firmly on the ground, and from this moment on, his dealings with Liana would be strictly business.

But even as he made the avowal, he couldn't stop himself from wondering if her lips were as soft as they looked.

LIANA STOOD IN THE BACK ROOM of Linden Photo Processing and watched the machine as it spit out her prints. As she'd known, only the photos of that magnificent late-morning sunrise were spectacular, and she splayed them out across the table and peered down at them. Their beauty brought tears to her eyes and she swiped at them impatiently with the back of her hand.

Sam had wanted to bring his grandfather the beauty of spring in the Rocky mountains, and she knew that the photographs in front of her were a step in that direction. But it was a picture of Sam framed against the mountains behind him that caught her attention. He was magnificent. Anyone else would have been dwarfed by the backdrop, but he dominated his surroundings. His stance, feet braced apart and arms akimbo, said he was invincible and ready to take on the world to prove it.

She trailed her fingers over his image, and then brought it to her lips as she recalled their almost kiss. She knew it was his emanating strength and security that drew her to him. He was like a port in a storm, offering a protective haven, and she yearned for that. She also knew instinctively that Sam was not the type of man to form a casual alliance.

She had to keep her distance from him, she told herself firmly. He might give her what she yearned for, but he'd demand a commitment in return, and she could never offer that to Sam or any man. A commitment meant being ready, willing and able to risk your life for the other person, and she'd already proved that she was incapable of that ultimate sacrifice.

Chapter Four

While waiting for Sam to arrive, Liana paced in her living room, trying to decide how she should greet him. If she wasn't cool, he might think she was encouraging him and would attempt to kiss her again but if she treated him too coolly, he might think he'd insulted her and try to apologize, and he certainly didn't owe her an apology.

She was still struggling with the problem when the doorbell rang. She approached the door reluctantly, wishing she had more time to reach a decision. She plastered on what she hoped was a neutral expression and prayed for the best.

But the moment Liana opened the door, she discovered that she'd been worrying for nothing. Sam met her gaze with the same polite look of the day before, and his tone was equally polite when he said, "Good morning, Liana. Are you ready to go?"

Confusion flowed through her because she found herself torn in two different directions. One part of her was flooded with relief that he wasn't upset, but another part was oddly disconcerted by his behavior. Was it possible that she'd read more into what she'd perceived had happened? Maybe the man hadn't tried to kiss her after all. Maybe it had been nothing more than her imagination.

"Yes, I'm ready to go, but I have yesterday's photographs if you'd like to look at them."

His eyes registered surprise. "You've developed them already?"

Liana nodded. "I manage a photo finishing store, so I have immediate access to all the necessary equipment. The light's the best in the kitchen, and while you look at them, I can whip up some pancakes so we won't have to stop for breakfast. It might save us some time."

Now why had she offered to cook pancakes? she wondered. She'd had no intention of fixing him breakfast, and it definitely wasn't a way to maintain her distance. But she couldn't very well withdraw the offer, even though her common sense told her that was exactly what she should do.

Sam resisted the urge to plow his hand through his hair. He didn't know which he found more surprising. The fact that she already had the photographs processed, or that she was offering to feed him breakfast. He'd come here determined to deal with her on a strictly business level, and she'd thrown him a curve ball. If he turned down her offer of breakfast, then he'd appear to be irked about their parting last night, but if he accepted it, he'd be tacitly agreeing to a more informal relationship between them, and that, he knew, he couldn't afford to do. He was too intrigued with Liana to deal with her in any way but on a formal employer-employee basis.

His common sense told him to tell her he'd already eaten, but he knew that within a few hours his stomach would be confirming the lie, so he said, "Pancakes sound good. And you're right. It will save us some time."

"Anything for the cause," she responded, and gestured him inside.

While Liana gathered the makings for pancakes, Sam spread the photographs across her breakfast counter. He let out a low, appreciative whistle as his gaze moved from one photograph to the next. Spectacular was the closest word he could come up with to describe them, but even it seemed inadequate when faced with the beauty before him.

"These are good, Liana. Really good," he told her.

She glanced up from pouring flour into a mixing bowl. "The only really good ones are of that late-morning sunrise. The remainder of them are just okay."

Sam studied the photographs again, and he decided that if she thought everything but the late-morning sunrise was "just okay," he'd burn his personal photo album before he ever let her get her hands on it.

"I think they're wonderful. What's wrong with them?"

She finished adding the remaining ingredients to her pancake batter, and then carried the bowl over to where he stood. Cradling the bowl in her arms, she stirred the mixture, saying, "There's no real texture or composition to them. Look at the ones of the meadow. That outcropping of rock in the left-hand corner should have been the focal point instead of an added attraction. Not only would it add more depth to the picture, but it would also emphasize the fragility of the flowers. I should have picked that up, but I'm afraid I'm out of practice."

Sam chuckled and gave a wry shake of his head. "I should be so out of practice." He then gave her a teasing grin as he said, "I should also be terribly offended."

Startled by his words, Liana's eyes widened. "Offended? Why?"

He tapped the photograph of himself. "I've never been accused of lacking texture or having no composition before."

Liana almost laughed, and probably would have if she hadn't forgotten how. "Your texture and composition are fine, Sam," she assured. "It's the mountain that's in trouble."

"I'm tempted, but I think I'll opt for valor and leave that line alone," he said as he piled the photographs together and slid them back into the envelope.

He watched her as she sat the bowl on the counter and began to put her cooking supplies away. "You make pancakes from scratch?

"Yes. Why does that surprise you?"

"Because no one makes pancakes from scratch anymore. Haven't you seen those boxes where you dump a cup or two of mix into a bowl, add some water, and voilà, you have pancakes?"

"Sure," Liana answered. "I've also read the ingredients on those boxes, and the way I see it, anything that requires a chemistry degree to know what I'm eating is something to be avoided."

"You're a health-food nut," he accused mildly.

She shook her head as she opened the door of the refrigerator and searched the shelves. "Nope. I'm just someone who likes to keep things simple. Besides, I flunked chemistry twice in high school, and I refuse to be reminded of that humiliation by being forced to look up words that tell me I'm eating salt and sugar. Do you want strawberry jam or maple syrup?"

"I'll have whatever you're having," he said, enjoying the sight of her rounded derriere as she bent to retrieve the topping she'd chosen.

When she rose, she turned toward him with a huge bottle of syrup. "Pure maple syrup from Vermont. No preservatives and no additives. Think your system can handle it?"

"Well, if it can't, my life is in your hands. I hope you're trained in CPR."

She paled and something flashed in her eyes. It was dark and resembled pain, but before Sam could actually analyze the emotion, she turned her back on him and said, "Why don't you have a seat? We'll be ready to eat in a few minutes."

Sam did run his hand through his hair at that moment, and it took every bit of his willpower to hold back the curse that was trembling on his lips. For the past ten or fifteen minutes she'd been chattering away like a normal human being. Then one lousy comment, and she'd withdrawn back into her shell. What in the world was the matter with her?

He considered pushing the issue, but then decided that there was no reason to make a tense situation more tense. He also decided that from now on he'd abide by his orginal decision. He'd deal with Liana on a strictly objective level. There'd be no more breakfasts or chatty conversations. He'd only speak when spoken to, outside of any normal amenities that were needed to preclude being rude, of course. If Liana wanted to play peek-a-boo with the world, then she'd have to find someone else to be her straight man.

And if he believed that, he knew he might as well start buying bridges.

SAM STARED OUT THE WINDOW while his grandfather shuffled through the photographs Liana had given him that morning. The pictures had accomplished what he'd hoped they would. His grandfather had perked up and was showing more animation than he had in months. So why, Sam wondered, did he feel so depressed?

"Look at this one, Sam."

Sam turned from the window to look at one of the photographs his grandfather was holding of the late-morning sunrise, and he frowned as he recalled how much those shots had cost her. The memory also brought back the deviling questions that had been tormenting him since he'd met her. Why had she retired from photography? Why had she withdrawn from life? And why did he even want to know?

"If you don't like the picture, just say so," his grandfather said. "Don't glare at it until it goes up in smoke."

Sam gave the old man a wry smile. "I like the picture. I was just thinking."

"With thoughts like that, you're going to develop one heck of a headache. What's wrong?"

Sam shook his head. "Nothing." Then he sighed and said, "That's a bald-faced lie."

His grandfather chuckled for the first time in weeks. "I know that. Talk, son. If nothing else, you'll get it off your chest."

Sam dropped into a chair across from his grandfather, knowing that talking was exactly why he'd come tonight. He'd intended to wait until he had a huge packet of pictures before giving them to the old man, but this morning's little scene with Liana was driving him up a wall.

"I've met this woman," he said. When his grandfather's lips curved into a grin, he quickly added. "Not that kind of woman, Gramps. She's just a business associate."

"Sure," his grandfather agreed, but Sam could hear the amused skepticism in his voice.

Deciding to ignore it, Sam sat forward, braced his arms on his knees and linked his fingers together. "Something bad has happened to her, Gramps. Something so bad that it's eating her up inside. She's wallowing in winter, and I want to help her make a change of seasons. The trouble is, I don't know how to reach her."

"Making a change of seasons is not easy, Sam. Look how hard it was for you when your father died. You felt angry, frightened and abandoned, and the fact that he committed suicide intensified those feelings. The only reason I was able to help you find your way back was because there was a strong bond of love between us. You trusted me, even though you were fighting me with everything you had inside."

Sam stared down at his hands as he absorbed his grandfather's words, feeling uncomfortable, as usual, about references to his father's death. Even after twenty years, the memory still tormented him, and he wondered if he'd ever come to grips with it.

He pushed those troubling thoughts aside and said, "What you're saying is that I can only help her if she trusts me. But how do I make her trust me?"

"You know as well as I do that you can't make someone trust you. They have to come to that conclusion on their own. Also, this woman has to want to be saved, so the first thing you need to do is analyze her life. Who or what is in it to make her fight her way out of her depression?"

Sam rose to his feet and walked back to the window. As he stuffed his hands into his pockets, he said, "I don't know enough about her to tell you that. I don't know who her friends are or even if she has family. I just know that she's hurting. I keep telling myself that it isn't my problem, but she's so beautiful and so talented. She took the pictures I just gave you, and I hate to see all of that talent go to waste."

"Wanting to help her is commendable, Sam, but you also have to be realistic. It's possible that you'll fail, and you need to decide if you're strong enough to handle that. Quite frankly, I'm not sure that you are."

Sam spun around to face him, startled by his grandfather's comment. "Why do you say that?"

His grandfather smiled wistfully. "Sam, I know you as well as I know myself. Ever since Kay walked out on you,

you've built your life around me and your mother. Now, I'm ill without much hope for recovery, and Tom Harper has asked your mother to marry him. I think your need to help this woman may be stemming from a need to help yourself, to come to grips with all the changes that are happening in your life. If it is, then her failure could be your failure. Perhaps you should concentrate on yourself for now and deal with her later.''

It was then that Sam realized why he was depressed. His grandfather, as usual, had skipped the chase and gone right to the heart of the matter. He wasn't going to have the old man much longer and his mother was seriously considering marriage to Tom Harper, the man she'd been dating for more than a year. The only two people he trusted implicitly, loved unconditionally, were going to abandon him.

Tears stung his eyes, and he swung around to stare out the window. He was being childish, and he knew it. Death was a part of life, and if his mother remarried, she wouldn't be deserting him. She'd still be his mother, and she'd always be there for him.

But Sam knew himself well enough to understand that once she'd committed herself to marriage, he wouldn't feel comfortable burdening her with his problems. She'd had to face enough troubles in her life, and Sam wanted her to spend the remainder of it carefree and happy. If anyone could make that happen for her, it was Tom.

It suddenly dawned on him that his grandfather had just told him to look at Liana's life and determine who or what was in it to make her want to survive. If he took that one step further and looked at his own life, who or what did he have to make him want to survive?

The answer was too frightening to face, and he turned back to the old man, asking, ''Which of those pictures would you like framed?

LIANA SAT ON THE TOP STEP of her back porch and watched the stray tom cat cautiously approach the bowl of food sitting on the bottom step, a ritual they'd been performing for the past six months.

The cat, whom she'd refused to name, was orange and white, although the animal was so dirty that the latter color was an assumption rather than a known fact. Half of his right ear was gone, and his face was a crisscross of battle scars. The tip of his tail dropped at an unnatural angle, and he had a crippled front paw that gave him a noticeable limp. When he'd first appeared at her house, he'd had the gaunt look of starvation. Now he only looked scrawny. Liana had long ago decided that he was the ugliest cat she'd ever seen.

She supposed that was why she'd decided to feed him, even though she'd known that to feed a stray was to inherit it, and the last thing she wanted was a pet. However, she'd soon learned that the cat didn't want her anymore than she wanted him. He accepted her food, but he wouldn't let her near him.

When the cat finally reached the bowl, he sat back on his haunches and regarded her warily. Liana carried out the second part of the ritual by saying, "Eat in peace. I wouldn't touch you with a ten foot pole soaked in disinfectant."

The cat bobbed his head as if acknowledging her words, and then lowered it to the food.

While Liana watched him eat, she fingered the postcard from her mother that she'd tucked into her jacket pocket. When she'd first moved to Denver, her mother had sent her long, chatty letters once or twice a week. Then, as time passed and Liana hadn't responded, the letters had dwindled to one postcard a month with short, cryptic sentences of family news. Liana both dreaded and looked forward to receiving the simple communiqués. They were her last link to her family and she hadn't yet found the courage to sever it completely.

When the cat had finished eating, he once again sat back on his haunches and licked perfunctorily at his front paw before making a halfhearted effort at washing his face. As he went through the motions of grooming, Liana announced, "I got a postcard from my mother today. Would you like to hear her news?" The cat paused, looked up at her, and moved his shoulders in a manner that Liana would have described as a bored shrug in a human being. Taking his response as an affirmative answer, she pulled the postcard from her pocket and began to paraphrase the small, neat handwriting.

"My brother Sandy, and his wife still haven't had their baby. It's two weeks overdue and that must be driving Sandy crazy. He's a stickler for punctuality," she editorialized before moving on to the next sentence.

"My sister Adriane is threatening to quit school again, which drives Mom crazy. She wants to see her well-educated and independent. Even for Mom, that may be a pipe-dream. Adriane is so spoiled rotten that I doubt she'd be able to hold down a job.

"Hey, Dad just won the senior's golf tournament at the country club. That's four years in a row. Mom says he's so proud he can hardly keep the buttons from popping off his shirt.

"That's it," she told the cat as she tucked the postcard back into her pocket and stared unseeingly at the weathered redwood fence that enclosed her backyard. "As usual, Mom didn't say anything about herself."

And, as usual, that very fact disturbed Liana. Her mother was active in a handful of charities, and she'd never been shy about boasting of her philanthropic victories. But in the past three months, she hadn't made one reference to her good works, which, more than anything else, had Liana convinced that something was wrong.

She was sorely tempted to go inside and call home to find out what was going on, but the impulse was quelled by the memory of the horror on her parents' faces when she'd told them about Bill and South America. She was sure her parents had accepted what she had done, because that was the kind of selfless act parents performed. She also knew that acceptance was not forgiveness, which, she was sure, they would never be able to give her. If she broke her silence now, they'd think that she was trying to make peace, and she'd only end up hurting them more when they learned that she wasn't extending the olive branch, but merely satisfying her curiosity.

With a heavy sigh, Liana rested her elbows on her knees and cradled her chin in her hands, wishing that she'd never gotten the postcard in the first place. Or, better yet, that she could be magically transported back in time so she could change...

"Knock, knock," a male voice said, intruding into her thoughts.

So startled that she nearly fell off the steps, Liana twisted around to confront her unexpected visitor.

"I'm sorry. I didn't mean to scare you," Sam said as he walked into her backyard and let the gate close behind him. "I rang the bell, but no one answered. Then I saw the light back here and thought I'd investigate. I'm taking the photographs over to my grandfather tonight and decided to stop by and see if today's pictures are ready. It'll save me a trip."

Sam knew he was babbling. He was also lying through his teeth. He hadn't come for the pictures, and he'd just left his grandfather. The meeting had left him unsettled, and he'd had this overwhelming need to see Liana.

Lord, she was beautiful, he thought as he watched her rise to her feet. The yellow bulb in her porch light emphasized the highlights in her brown hair and added an exotic tint to her rich bronze complexion. As she stared at him, her eyes dark and wary, Sam realized that his decision to deal with her on a strictly business level had been for naught. He couldn't any more distance himself from Liana than he could swim the Atlantic ocean.

He was crazy, he told himself. She didn't want anything to do with him. But then, again, it was apparent that she didn't want anything to do with anyone, and he would be remiss if he let her bury herself in oblivion. Her talent was rare, and he inwardly shuddered at the thought of what mankind would lose if it didn't have her insight into its existence.

As he had told his grandfather, it was time for Liana to undergo a change of seasons, and he was going to help her make the transition. The trick would be protecting himself while performing the task.

"That's an ugly cat," he commented when Liana maintained her silence.

Liana automatically glanced down at the cat, surprised to see that he was still there pretending to bathe. He was normally so skittish that the slightest noise would send him running. She didn't like the fact that he'd not only failed to alert her to Sam's arrival, but that he seemed completely at ease with Sam's presence.

"He's a stray," she said.

"A stray doesn't have a home, and this old guy has definitely found a home here, haven't you?" Sam said as he squatted and wiggled his fingers, encouraging the cat to come to him.

"He's afraid of people," Liana informed him. "He won't let anyone near him."

The cat, as if determined to prove her a liar, promptly limped his way to Sam and let him scratch his ears.

Sam gave her an impudent grin. "I guess he's feeling sociable tonight."

Liana shot an admonishing look at the cat, deciding that if this was all the loyalty she got after saving the scruffy animal from starvation, then she wasn't going to waste any more money on those tiny, expensive cans of gourmet cat food. From now on he could eat plain fare and be satisfied with it.

"I wouldn't get too close to him," she told Sam. "As I said, he's a stray, and he's probably riddled with disease."

Sam chuckled and the cat gave her a smug look before giving an insouciant swish of his tail and lifting his chin for a scratch. Sam complied with the request as he once again grinned at Liana.

"He's probably harboring some fleas and a few undesirable parasites, but I don't think I'll catch anything from him."

Liana had a couple of good comebacks for that line, but decided to keep them to herself. Besides, the way Sam kept grinning at her, he was probably trying to get a rise out of her.

"I'll go get the pictures," she stated irritably.

"Great." Sam gave the cat one last scratch before standing and walking toward her. "I can't wait to see them."

That wasn't an invitation to come in, Liana railed inwardly, but didn't voice the objection. Sam was playing some kind of game with her and she had yet to figure out what it was.

She entered the house without waiting for him and headed for the entry closet to retrieve the pictures. When she pulled them out, she waited, expecting Sam to join her. After several minutes had passed and he hadn't shown up, she went looking for him. He was in the kitchen, the cat curling around his legs as he fixed the animal another plate of food.

"What's *he* doing in here?" Liana asked sharply.

Sam slowly pivoted his head toward her, one brow arched in question. "He's still hungry. Is there a problem?"

Hell, yes, there's a problem, Liana thought. It was bad enough that Sam had breached her defenses, but by bringing the cat into the house, he was also breaching her home. It was something she couldn't let happen, because this was her last stronghold against the world and it had to remain antiseptic. Cat hair scattered throughout the house hardly met that definition. But how could she throw the cat out when Sam was standing there looking as if he expected her to do just that?

She gritted her teeth and said, "No, there isn't a problem. I was just surprised to see him in here."

"He's a pretty good cat, even if he is as beat-up as a punchy prizefighter," Sam commented as he set the plate of food on the floor. "If you took him to the vet, got him his shots and maybe even neutered, you'd have a good pet."

Liana scowled at the cat. "I don't have time for a pet. Besides, he doesn't like me. Why don't you take him home with you?"

"My apartment building doesn't allow pets, and what do you mean he doesn't like you?"

Liana rolled her eyes toward the ceiling, praying for patience. "He won't even let me touch him, Sam. All he does is eat my food."

"Maybe he's just waiting for another man's opinion of your character." Sam grinned at her again. "You know, picking a pet owner is like choosing a spouse. You need to make sure that you communicate on the same wavelength."

"Believe me, Sam. I'm not good spouse material."

Sam chuckled. "I don't think he wants to marry you, Liana. He just wants to live with you."

But I don't want him living with me! Liana silently roared. Aloud, she said, "Here are the pictures."

Sam walked across the kitchen, took them from her and settled himself into her booth. Liana knew she should take a seat, but she was too restless. Instead, she turned and eyed the traitorous cat distrustfully. He wasn't gulping down his food as he normally did, but was taking his time, savoring his meal.

Darn cat, she thought in disgust.

"Hooligan," Sam said.

Liana glanced over her shoulder at him. "What?"

"You should call him Hooligan." Sam nooded toward the cat.

"Look at him. Doesn't he resemble a hooligan?"

What he resembled was a normalcy that Liana wasn't about to let enter her life. The moment Sam left, she was going to toss the animal out the door, assuming, of course, that she'd be able to catch him. She also wasn't about to name him, and it was time to change the subject.

"I don't have a cat box," she announced.

"A cardboard box with a shredded newspaper will get him through the night," Sam said.

"I don't have a cardboard box, or a newspaper, for that matter," she countered smugly.

"That's easily rectified. We'll run down to the nearest mall. Someone will have a cat box and litter."

"He could have rabies," Liana offered.

"He isn't foaming at the mouth," Sam noted. "Are you afraid of him, Liana?"

"Of course not."

"Great. Then let's go get him a cat box."

Liana was feeling cornered and desperate. "Sam, I really don't have time for a pet."

"How much time does a cat require? Come on, Liana. He needs a litter box and a bowl of food. From there on out, it'll be a piece of cake."

"Who's going to take care of him when we go into the mountains for four days?" she asked, latching onto the first good excuse she could think of to toss the cat outside where he belonged.

"Your neighbors?"

"I've never met my neighbors, and I'm not about to start an acquaintance by asking them to care for my cat."

Sam smothered a smile. The fact that she'd referred to the animal with a possessive pronoun told him volumes. She cared for the cat, even if she wasn't ready to admit it. Before he left tonight, he was going to have Hooligan moved in, because intuition told him that as long as Liana managed to maintain the sterility of her mausoleum, she wouldn't make any effort to move forward with her life. The presence of the cat would disrupt her order. She'd have to feed him, clean his box, and acknowledge his presence, because Sam knew there was nothing peskier than a cat who believed he was being ignored. Hooligan would demand attention to right the wrong, even if he normally abhorred attention.

"I'll find someone to take care of him while we're gone."

"I can't let you to do that."

"Why not? You are working for me. We'll just consider it one of the perks of the job."

"We didn't contract for perks," she snapped.

"We didn't contract at all," he corrected calmly.

Her temper finally erupted. "Dammit, Sam, I don't want the responsibility of that cat!"

He leaned back in the booth and laced his hands behind his head. "You have been feeding him, so I'd say you've already taken on that responsibility. And whether you keep him inside or outside, someone is going to have to feed him while we're gone. Or were you going to abandon him and let the poor guy fend for himself?"

Liana knew she'd walked into Sam's trap with both eyes open, and she wanted to scream in frustration. If she admitted that she had intended to let the cat fend for himself while she was gone, she'd sound callous. But her only other option was to accept responsibility for the animal, which would make her a member of the human race again and she'd already turned in her membership card.

She glared at Sam so murderously that he should have been shaking in his boots. Instead, the fool was smiling at her.

"That cat is filthy, and you said yourself that he probably has fleas," she said truculently.

Sam shrugged. "So, we'll give him a bath and pick up a flea collar."

Liana ground her teeth. He had an answer for everything and she was running out of objections. "Why are you insisting that I adopt a cat that doesn't like me?"

"If he doesn't like you, why is he rubbing against your legs?"

Liana had been so intent on deflecting Sam's efforts at installing the cat in the house that she hadn't even realized the animal was rubbing against her. She was so surprised that she leaped back. The cat simply followed her, resumed his rubbing and began to purr.

It was the purr that was Liana's undoing and she caught her lower lip between her teeth as it began to tremble. Like it or not, she now had a pet.

"How do you give a cat a bath?" she asked, a strange quiver in her voice as she stared down at Hooligan.

"Very carefully," Sam answered, and his heart gave a little lurch when Liana looked up at him and smiled. It wasn't a full-blown, show-the-teeth smile, but it was a smile. Sam had never seen anything so beautiful in his life, and he knew that he was going to drag her out of her depression if he had to do it with her kicking and screaming.

He also knew he had to get out of here before he did something really crazy, like pull Liana into his arms and kiss her until she couldn't breathe.

"I'll go pick up a cat box, litter and a flea collar," Sam said as he rose to his feet. "You'd better stay here and keep an eye on Hooligan. We wouldn't want him to have an accident before we get his facilities installed."

Before Liana could offer him money to make the purchases, Sam rushed out the back door. She stared at the door curiously, and then glanced down at the cat. "What do you think that was all about?" she asked him.

Hooligan paused in his rubbing long enough to give her one of his bored shrugs. Liana chuckled softly and bent to pet him. The cat wasn't much to look at, but he was hers. The thought caused a pleasant, warm feeling inside.

"SAM, ARE YOU SURE you know what you're doing?" Liana asked as she closed the bathroom door while he filled the tub.

Hooligan was sitting on the floor beside Sam, completely oblivious to his upcoming fate, and Liana searched her mind, trying to recall whether she had any first-aid cream and bandages.

"Sure I'm sure," he answered cheerfully as he lifted a bottle of flea shampoo from the floor. "No tears," he announced, holding the bottle up for inspection.

"It's not tears I'm worried about," she muttered. "It's scars."

Sam turned off the faucet, tested the water, and then rolled up his shirt sleeves. "This is going to be a piece of cake, Liana."

"The last time I heard that, my brother had me climbing a tree to fetch his kite and I fell and broke my arm."

"You have a brother?" Sam asked nonchalantly, tucking the information away. It could be valuable in his quest to bring Liana back to the land of the living.

"Yeah."

"What's his name?"

"Henry Terrance Stevens, VI. He goes by Sandy for short."

"I don't blame him," Sam said as he sat back on his heels and studied Hooligan, trying to decide the best way to introduce the cat to a bath. He wouldn't have admitted it under torture, but he, too, feared a few scars. "Any other brothers?"

"No. I have a sister who's named Adriane, but it should be Trouble. She was a midlife surprise, and my parents have indulged her to the point that she's impossible."

Sam glanced up at her and grinned. "Daughters should be indulged to the point that they're impossible. Have you got a blow dryer in here?"

"Yes. Why?"

"The people at the pet store said we should get Hooligan as dry as possible so he doesn't get sick. They recommended a blow dryer."

Liana studied the cat warily. "If you can get him through wash and rinse, I suppose I can get him through fluff dry."

"It's a deal," he said. Then he turned his attention to the cat. "Well, Hooligan, it's show time. You behave, and I'll give you a treat. Just to get you into the mood, it's fish-flavored and crunchy."

The cat growled as Sam lifted him and stuck his back feet into the water.

The growl sounded so deadly that Liana shivered. "Sam, maybe this isn't such a good idea."

"Sure, it's a good idea," he said as he lowered the cat even further into the water. "You and I have an understanding, don't we, Hooligan? A clean cat is a healthy cat. It's also a cat that has a roof over his head come rain or sleet or snow. Growl if you must. Just keep the claws sheathed."

To Liana's amazement, Hooligan did just that. He continued to growl low in his throat, and it still sent shivers racing through her, but not once did he strike out at Sam, even when he poured water over the animal's head, carefully keeping it out of his eyes and ears.

Liana also couldn't help but feel sorry for the poor cat. If he'd looked scrawny before, he now looked pitiful with his hair plastered against his body. When he trembled, she was sure he was freezing to death, and she hauled her blow dryer out of the cabinet and turned it on so it would be warm when she took over. She sat on the toilet to wait.

Eventually, Sam lifted the cat out of the tub and rubbed him down briskly with a towel. Then he said, "Your turn," and passed Hooligan to Liana.

She settled Hooligan on her lap, wet towel and all, and crooned to him softly as she whisked the blow dryer over him.

Sam opened the drain on the tub and then sat on its edge as he watched Liana. Her attention was totally trained on the cat, and he listened to her murmur to him, her face soft and her hands gentle as she manipulated the animal so she could reach every wet spot. The angry twitch of his tail made it evident that Hooligan wasn't any more impressed with his blow dry than he'd been with his bath, but at least he'd stopped growling, Sam noted.

"I think this is going to be a one-time accommodation," Liana said when she finally finished and Hooligan immediately leaped off her lap. He stalked toward the door, his nose lifted haughtily.

Sam chuckled, leaned over and opened the door so the cat could exit. "He'll be fine. You should get him to the vet, though. He needs his shots and a good physical exam. Make an appointment, and if we need to take a day off so you can take care of him, that'll be fine."

"You're a nice man, Sam," she said as she perched her elbows on her knees, cradled her chin in her hands and blessed him with another smile.

"Well, it's a tough job, but someone's got to do it," he said gruffly as he rose to his feet, suddenly needing to escape the room as badly as Hooligan had. She looked so sweet and approachable, but Sam knew it was an unconscious invitation. "Let's get him into that flea collar and set up his cat box."

It took some coaxing and a handful of fish-flavored treats to get Hooligan into the collar, but Sam finally managed it. He also prepared his cat box.

By the time he was done, he knew he had to call it a night. He'd become too aware of Liana on a physical level as she'd hovered around him and the cat, trying to help, but only setting his nerves on edge whenever she brushed against him.

But it was her gentleness and concern that touched him the most. It was a part of her he hadn't seen, and yet it was a part that he'd known intuitively existed. He also heard his grandfather's voice echoing in his ears. *The first thing you need to do is analyze her life. Who or what is in it to make her fight her way out of her depression?*

With any luck, Sam had given her some impetus tonight.

"I have to go," he told her reluctantly.

"Oh, of course!" Liana exclaimed guiltily. She glanced toward the clock. "I hope it's not too late to visit your grandfather."

Sam blinked, confused for a moment by her comment, but then recalling his lie when he'd arrived. "It's not too late."

"Good. Let me get the photographs, and, of course, I want to pay you for Hooligan's supplies."

"Forget the supplies," Sam said. "They're on me."

"Don't be ridiculous," Liana said as she picked up the bag that had held all the cat paraphernalia, noted the amount on the receipt stapled to it and hauled her wallet out of her purse. She pressed the money into his hand.

Sam stared down at the money, feeling angry, and he wasn't certain why. The cat was hers, and she had every right to reimburse him for the supplies. And yet there was an elemental part of him balking against the act. He told himself he was being ridiculous, but he felt as if he were being shoved aside because he was no longer useful.

But before he could work himself into a fine temper, Liana laid her hand on his arm and said, "I can't thank you enough, Sam. I could have never handled Hooligan on my own."

Sam had read a line somewhere about "falling into someone's eyes," but until now he'd always considered it romantic fancy. The warm sincerity glowing in the depths of Liana's big brown eyes was like a physical touch, and he felt it all the way down to the tips of his toes. A fine tremor shook his hand and he fought against the need to brush his fingertips against her long lashes to discover if they were as silken as they looked.

"It was my pleasure," he said as he stuffed the money into his pocket and accepted the envelope of photographs she handed him. "I'll see you tomorrow."

Liana nodded, scooped Hooligan up into her arms and walked Sam to the door.

When he backed out of her drive, he glanced back at her house. She and Hooligan were standing in the doorway, no more than dark silhouettes against the light pouring out the front door, but Sam would have sworn that both of them were smiling at him.

Chapter Five

"Sam, be careful!" Liana exclaimed worriedly when his foot slipped while he tried to scale the face of a rugged cliff.

Once he had himself steadied, Sam glanced over his shoulder at her and grinned. "Stop worrying, Liana. I told you, I'm half mountain goat."

"Well, that's not the half I'm worried about," she grumbled. "And why are you insisting on climbing that pile of rubble anyway?"

"You'll see," he said mysteriously.

He made it up another two or three feet when his foot slipped again, and Liana closed her eyes, refusing to watch his perilous ascent any longer. He wasn't high enough to plunge to his death, but he was high enough to break a few bones. How in the world was she supposed to get him out of here if he did? And why in the world had she let him climb the stupid cliff in the first place?

Because Sam was determined to do it, and if she'd learned nothing else about him, it was that when he was determined to do something, nothing outside of an armored tank was going to stop him.

"You can stop being a cowardly lion and open your eyes now," Sam called down to her.

She did as he instructed while chanting, "Sticks and stones may break my bones, but names will never hurt me."

Sam, who was sitting on a narrow ledge about fifteen feet above her, burst into laughter. "Now, that was original, Liana."

"I thought it was quite appropriate for the occasion," she said, feigning a haughty sniff.

"Mmm. Maybe it was."

He braced his hands on the ledge and swung his feet while he smiled down at her, and Liana experienced a strange melting sensation in the center of her chest. The wind had caught his hair and was blowing it across his forehead, giving him a rakish, piratical look. The excited gleam in his eyes and the devil-may-care grin on his lips only enhanced the picture, and when he leaped lithely to his feet and rested his hands on his hips, Liana decided that she'd never seen a man look so wildly gorgeous. She snapped his picture before he could object.

"Hey, what did I tell you about wasting your film on me?" he chided fondly.

"I'm not wasting it. It was a good shot. Now, how about coming down from there so we can get back to work."

"We're going to work from up here."

"*We're* going to from up there?" Liana repeated. Then she shook her head. "I don't climb cliffs, Sam. There is no mountain goat in my lineage."

He chuckled as he shed his day pack and Liana watched him open it and pull out a rope.

"What are you doing?" she asked suspiciously as he looped one end of it.

"I'm tying a bowline knot," he answered.

"What for?"

He waggled his brows at her. "Why, to drag you up here, of course."

Liana took a wary step back. "I'm not the dragging kind of woman, Sam."

"Don't knock it until you've tried it." He anchored one end of the rope to a rock and lowered the looped end down to her. "Slip it around your waist and tighten the knot. Then I'll pull you up."

"No way," Liana said with a firm shake of her head. "I'm a lot heavier than I look. You'll drop me on my head."

"I won't drop you. Trust me."

Trust me. The words ricocheted through Liana's mind and she was suddenly thrust back in time. Bill was clasping her upper arms, his expression persuasive and pleading. *Nothing will happen, Liana. I swear, nothing will happen. Trust me.*

"Liana?" Sam said in concern as he watched her face suddenly pale. "Liana!" he said more sharply when she didn't respond.

She looked up at him. "What?"

"Are you okay?"

She brushed her hand over her eyes and nodded. "I'm fine."

"You're sure?"

"I'm sure."

Despite her assurances, however, Sam wasn't convinced. Some of her color had returned, but she still looked pale. "It's obvious that you're not feeling well. I'll come down and we'll go home."

"No!" Liana blushed when she realized that she'd shouted the word. "No," she repeated calmly. "I'm fine, Sam. Really. I just felt a little dizzy for a moment. It's probably the thin mountain air."

Before he could respond, she grabbed the rope and secured it around her waist. "I'm ready when you are. Just remember that I have a fortune's worth of camera equipment on me. If you drop me and break it, I'll sue."

"Good heavens, who would have ever believed that litigation has corrupted the ranks of nature photographers," Sam teased, but he wasn't feeling one bit humorous.

Something had happened down there, and it had nothing to do with thin mountain air. As he began to haul her up the cliff, he recalled the morning she'd cooked him pancakes. She'd been exchanging lighthearted banter with him then, too, and, just as she'd done today, she'd suddenly paled. There had to be a connection between the two conversations, but no matter how hard he tried, he couldn't figure out what it was.

"Things just keep getting curiouser and curiouser with you, don't they, my sweet?" he muttered beneath his breath, deciding that Liana was right. She was heavier than she looked.

A few minutes later he pulled her over the edge and helped her to her feet. Then he searched her face, relieved to see that all her color had returned. For a moment he considered questioning her about what had happened, particularly since she was avoiding eye contact with him. But he'd brought her up here to show her something special, and he didn't want to destroy the moment with a confrontation.

"Follow me," he said as he put his pack on and angled his way along the ledge. "And watch where you're going. That first step down is a long one."

Liana clung to the side of the cliff, experiencing a momentary flash of vertigo when she peered down at the ground. She closed her eyes and drew in several deep breaths. She wasn't afraid of heights, but she was terrified of narrow ledges. After all, as Sam had said, it was a long first step down, and how was she supposed to know if the next step she took wouldn't land on a weak spot, cause a landslide and send her flying.

"Sam, where are you?" she called out when she opened her eyes and found him gone.

"Right around the corner. Hurry up, Liana. We don't have all day."

"Hurry up, Liana. We don't have all day," she mimicked irritably as she began to ease her way along the ledge.

This was the last of her mountain goat days, she vowed as she came to the corner. She'd agreed to hike and take pictures, not risk life and limb—or at least limb—so Sam could indulge his cloven-hoof tendencies.

When she rounded it, the ledge became a large plateau, and Sam stood in the mouth of a cave at the other end of it.

"Come on. Hurry up," he encouraged.

Liana held her ground and shook her head. She was a good sport, and she'd go along with a little mountain goating. She was not, however, into spelunking, and Sam couldn't get her to set foot in that cave if he offered her a million bucks.

"I refuse to go anywhere where a mining hat is considered haute couture," she told him staunchly.

He chuckled. "Afraid of the dark?"

"No. Just things that go bump in it."

"You don't have to go in. Just come over and have a peek inside," he encouraged.

"Well, maybe a peek. But that's it, Sam. I do not do caves."

He flashed her a sexy grin and treated her to a long, slow look that covered her from head to toe. "You're always handing me enough line to hang myself. You'd better be careful, because one of these days I just might take you up on the challenge."

Liana swallowed hard at the blatant sexual come on. She knew Sam was sexy, of course, but it was the first time she'd ever responded to him on that level. It was downright shocking to discover that her libido was still alive and well.

Instinct told her to hightail it out of there as fast as possible, but common sense kept her rooted in place. Good heavens, he was only indulging in a little harmless flirting. If he was serious, he would have made a move before now. They had, after all, been up in the mountains alone every day for nearly a week, and the only pass he'd made at her was to hand her a bag of trail mix.

She walked across the plateau, watching him from behind her lashes. Leaning against one wall of the cave, he crossed his arms over his chest and patiently waited for her.

When she reached him, she peered inside the cave. The moment she did, she forgot all about Sam's little flirtation and gasped in delight.

The cave was not a cave, but a tunnel about eight feet long with a bubbling mountain spring at the other end whose overflow shot out the other opening.

"It's the head of a waterfall!" Liana gasped as she rushed inside.

"I thought you were afraid of caves," Sam commented as he strolled in after her.

She spun around to face him. "You're a rat, Sam Dillon. A nice one, but a rat just the same. Why didn't you tell me this was up here?"

Because then I would have missed that wonderful look of excitement on your face, he answered inwardly. Aloud, he said, "I thought it would be a nice surprise."

"How did you ever find it?" Liana asked as she walked to the spring and looked out the opening. The vista in front of her was breathtaking, and she could only shake her head in awe. Magnificent outcroppings of granite were scattered all the way down to a pine-forested valley that stretched across miles to another mountain peak. Low fluffy clouds hung low over the valley, giving it a look of fairy-tale enchantment.

"I didn't find it," Sam said as he came up behind her. "My grandfather did, and he shared it with me. It's a fantastic view by day, but you should see it at night. The stream in the valley is filled with phosphorus and it glows in the dark. The stars are so large and brilliant that you feel as if you can reach up and pluck them right out of the sky. Gramps calls this his own secret little spot in heaven and refuses to believe that anyone else even knows it's here. That's ridiculous, of course. The waterfall alone would attract explorers, but it's a harmless indulgence on his part."

Liana nodded as she said, "My grandmother always said that if you want something to be magical and you believe in it with all your heart, then it will be magical to you, even if it isn't magical to anyone else."

"You've spoken of your grandparents often. You must have been very close to them," Sam said.

"They were the best friends I ever had," Liana replied as she leaned her head against the cool stone of hollowed-out rock. "My father used to grumble that they acted like Peter Pan and Tinker Bell, and he was forever asking them when they were going to grow up." She glanced up at Sam and gave him a poignant smile. "Thank heavens, they never did."

Involuntarily, Sam reached out and brushed strands of hair away from her face. "And what about you?" he asked softly. "Have you grown up?"

"Yes," she answered, her smile growing sad. "What about you?"

"I grew up a long time ago, but being grown up doesn't have to be a curse, Liana. It can be magical if you want it to be."

"I suppose you're right," she stated quietly, unaware that the timbre of her voice said she didn't believe him at all.

She pushed away from the wall and knelt on the edge of the spring. As she stared out over the view in front of her, she began mentally creating photographic images that she would record on film. It was a process she'd started during her trips into the mountains with Sam, because the actual use of her camera was still difficult. By creating the images, she was able to prepare herself mentally to lift her camera and put it to work.

She was unaware of Sam watching her, his brow furrowed as he tried to piece together the few puzzling clues she'd given about herself. It was only when she lifted her camera into her hands and began to shoot that he realized he'd spent close to a week with her and really knew nothing more about her than he'd known in the beginning. She was still an enigma, and he wondered if she always would be.

LIANA GLARED AT HOOLIGAN when he nearly tripped her for the third time in an hour. He'd been underfoot since the moment she'd walked into the house, and she was growing more annoyed with him by the minute. She'd fed him, given him fresh water and cleaned out his cat box. What more could the wretched animal want?

If Hooligan was affected by her ill-humor, he didn't show it. He merely plopped down on his rump and gazed at her placidly, his tail twitching slowly from side to side. Liana had the oddest feeling that he was issuing a challenge, and she decided to take him up on it.

She marched across the kitchen, threw open the door and said, "Get out."

Hooligan regarded her with one eye open and one eye closed. Then he lifted a front paw, licked it and diligently began to clean his face.

"I said get out," she stated more firmly.

Hooligan turned his back on her and resumed his grooming.

"Darn cat," she grumbled as she slammed the door closed, deciding that she'd at least gotten her point across. Leave her alone or leave the house.

Unfortunately, it appeared that Hooligan's memory was about half an inch long, because she no more than walked by him than he was back underfoot.

She stopped, propped her hands on her hips and glared down at him again. "Look, I've agreed to put a roof over your head and food in your mouth. In return, I expect you to stay out of my way. Got that?"

Hooligan purred and rubbed against her leg.

Liana rolled her eyes toward the ceiling and released a low cry of frustration, thinking that the cat was going to make her go completely insane. How was she supposed to suffer in peace when the animal wouldn't give her one moment to suffer?

She was still fuming when the doorbell rang, and she stormed through the house, sure it was Sam at the door. She'd told him she'd be developing the last two days' worth of photographs this evening, and he'd said he might stop by and pick them up. Well, she'd not only give him his photographs, but she'd also give him that darn cat he'd foisted off on her.

As she flung the door open, Neal thrust a big box into her arms and said, "Good. You're home. You carry this one. It's the lightest."

"What is this?" Liana asked as she peered into the box and discovered it was filled with plants.

"You're inheriting the ladies," Neal announced as he lifted a big box sitting at his feet and strolled into the house.

"These are plants!"

"African violets," he corrected, kicking the door closed and carrying his box into the middle of her living room. He set the box on the floor and then brushed his hands together, as if dusting them off. "Where do you want them?"

"Back where they came from," Liana answered with a glower.

Neal shook his head. "You have to keep them, Liana."

"But they're plants!" she all but screamed at him.

He grinned. "You've already made that observation. But these aren't just plants. These are African violets. I took them in as little sprouts and raised them to maturity. They've grown full and lush and bloomed their little heads off for me. Since I can't take them to London, I'm putting them in your care. You're the only person I know with enough room to take them all in, and I can't possibly split them up. It would be the same as breaking up a family."

Liana gaped at her friend. If it hadn't been for the somber expression on his face, she would have been sure he was joking. Understanding that he was totally serious made her blanch. She couldn't take plants into the house. Plants added color and clutter. Her rooms were purposely bland, because bland incited no thought, stimulated no imagination. She could wander from room to room without one brain cell even flickering.

"I have a black thumb, Neal. I'll kill them," she told him.

"No, you won't." He reached into his back pocket and pulled out a folded sheet of paper. "I've written down specific instructions. A three-year-old could take care of them by following my simple guidelines."

Liana set her box down on the floor and eyed him suspiciously. "Is this like one of those toys that any three-year-old can assemble, only they don't tell you that you need a three-year-old to do it?''

Neal grinned. "Why, Liana, you just made a joke."

"I'm not joking, Neal. I don't want your plants. I don't have time for your plants. I—"

"Where'd you get this ugly cat?"

Liana slumped her shoulders in defeat as Hooligan sidled up to Neal and rubbed against his pant leg. "He's a stray that's been hanging out in my backyard." She brightened when a sudden thought occurred to her. "Neal, I can't take your plants, because they might be poisonous to Hooligan."

"Naw," he said. "They're kid and pet proof. I made sure of that when I was dating Cindy. You remember Cindy, don't you?"

Boy, did Liana remember Cindy! She was a red-headed bombshell with three kids and a muscle-bound ex-husband who thought child support was having your kids cheer you on while you did a bench press. Cindy had chased after Neal with the bloodthirsty intent of a starving piranha. Thankfully, she'd gotten a peek at Neal's bank balance before he'd gotten around to popping the question. It was the only time Liana had seen Neal mourn over a lost love.

She supposed it was the memory of his heartache that made her soften. Or maybe it was just that she was feeling too overwhelmed to go into battle. Just a few days ago she'd climbed out of bed with her neat little world in perfect order. Now, she'd inherited a cat, who'd decided that contact companionship was the only way to go, and two boxes of pampered plants who thought they were ladies. But she supposed that after all Neal had done for her, she did owe him this much.

"All right, Neal. I'll take your plants."

"My ladies," he corrected.

"Yeah. Your ladies. Let me see your instructions."

When Neal handed her his instructions, Liana decided that the only three-year-old who could care for them would be one with a Ph.D. in horticulture. His instructions were more complicated than a computer flow chart, and she turned the paper upside down to see if it made better sense. It didn't.

"Neal, whatever happened to the good old days when you stuck a plant in a pot and gave it a drink of water once or twice a week?"

Neal gave her a horrified look. "My word, Liana, that's positively barbaric."

"So call me Conan."

He grinned again. "Two jokes in one day. What in the world has happened to you?"

What in the world *had* happened to her? Liana wondered at the realization that Neal was right. She had made a joke.

"Just explain these hieroglyphics," she muttered as she waved Neal's *simple* guidelines at him.

"Actually, it's very easy. I've assigned a number to each of the ladies and put it on her pot. You find her number, then match it to the chart. After that, you just follow the instructions."

Actually, it was simple, Liana decided after making a more critical review of the instructions. But as she continued to scan the list she frowned. "Sing to number 23? I couldn't carry a tune if my life depended upon it."

"So turn on the radio."

"I don't have a radio."

"I'll give you mine."

"I don't want a radio."

"You don't, but Petunia does."

Liana eyed him askance. "Petunia? I thought she was an African violet."

Neal brought a finger to his lips. "Shhh. She has an identity crisis."

"You're giving me a neurotic plant?"

"Seven," Neal answered. "Petunia, Daisy, Rose, Ivy..."

"I get the picture. I'll take your radio," she said, albeit grudgingly. It would be just one more piece of normalcy in her life that she'd managed to avoid. She was feeling more than a little bewildered at how the entrance of one scrawny cat into the house had caused a domino effect. If she wasn't careful, she'd be subscribing to the newspaper and putting pictures on the walls, for heaven's sake!

"Great. How about a cup of tea?" Neal said.

Liana nodded and led the way into the kitchen. Neal took a seat in the booth and watched as she filled the tea kettle and set it on the stove.

"It would be faster in a microwave," he noted as she turned away from the stove.

"I don't have a microwave," Liana reminded him.

"You should. A microwave is no longer a luxury. It's a necessity."

"Not for me."

Neal let out a melodramatic sigh when she slid into the booth across from him. "Why do you insist on living in the Dark Ages?"

Liana gave a dismissive shrug. "I prefer the Dark Ages. They were simpler times."

Neal shifted uncomfortably in his seat before saying, "We need to talk."

"About what?" Liana inquired, uneasy with his quick shift of mood.

"The bank. They say it will take at least forty-five days to approve your application to take over my loan. I'm due to leave in forty-eight days.

Liana frowned. "That means I'd have to submit all the paperwork this week."

"Yeah."

"I can't."

"Why not?"

"I won't have the money for another two and a half or three weeks. Can't the bank send the closing papers to you in London?"

"They could," Neal said. "But I need the money, Liana. You know me. A nickel burns a hole in my pocket. I have five dollars in my savings account, and my credit cards are charged to the max. I can manage a plane ticket to London, but once I'm there, I need a place to live. Flats don't come cheap."

"I'll loan you the money."

Neal shook his head. "You'll need every penny you can get your hands on to qualify for the loan."

Realizing the seriousness of the situation, Liana rested her forehead against the palm of her hand. "What do you expect me to do?"

"Ask Sam for a written contract. The bank said they'll accept a contract as proof of your assets and will tentatively approve the loan based upon it."

It took a moment for his words to sink in, and when they did, Liana lifted her head and glared at him. "How did you know about Sam?"

Neal raised both hands in a pacifying gesture. "Don't get your feathers all ruffled."

"It's not my ruffled feathers you need to worry about," she stated tightly at his complicity. "You sent him to me!"

Neal nodded.

"How could you do that to me? You knew how I felt about photography." When he didn't respond, she said, "I thought you were my friend."

"I am your friend."

"You sure have a funny way of showing it!"

"Dammit, Liana, grow up!" he fumed as he slapped his open palm down on the table, making Liana jump in surprise. She'd never heard Neal raise his voice, let alone seen him lose his temper.

He took advantage of her shock to continue, "Sam and I went to high school together, so it was only natural that he came to me when he was looking for a photographer. I knew then that I might be going to London. I also knew that if I did go, I wanted to give you first crack at the business. I suspected that you didn't have the money, so when he told me how much he was willing to pay, I figured what the heck. I'd send him your way and you'd either take the job or you wouldn't, but at least you'd have an option. If looking out for a friend's welfare is wrong, then I plead guilty, but I will not apologize for it."

Liana wanted to stay furious with him, but she couldn't. The sincere look on his face convinced her that his motivation for sending Sam to her had been altruistic, but she still felt manipulated.

"Why didn't you just come to me and tell me what was going on?" she asked disgruntledly.

"Pride," Neal answered as he leaned back in the booth. "I didn't tell a living soul about that interview because I was afraid I wouldn't get the job. You know that sympathy isn't my cup of tea. So, will you ask Sam for a contract?"

"I think you can ask him yourself," she stated as the doorbell rang. "That should be Sam now."

SAM WAS TRULY SHOCKED when he followed Liana into her kitchen and found Neal Linden sitting there sipping a cup of tea. When Neal had referred him to Liana, he hadn't given any indication that he'd personally known her, and since it was now apparent that he did, he had to have known that Liana was retired from photography. So why had Neal sent him to her?

Sam regarded the man suspiciously. He didn't like being used, especially by his friends, and he had the distinct feeling that he'd been manipulated with Machiavellian skill.

"I understand that the two of you are old friends, so I guess no introductions are necessary," Liana said.

"No, they aren't," Sam replied. "How are you, Neal?"

"Simply marvelous," Neal answered with a grin. "I've landed a job at *The London Times*, and I'll be leaving in about forty-eight days and nine hours," he said as he glanced down at his watch.

"Congratulations," Sam said, casting a quick look toward Liana. Were she and Neal involved? And, if so, was his imminent departure what had her so distraught?

It made perfect sense to Sam. After all, he knew firsthand how devastating it was to have someone you love walk away from you. It had taken him nearly a year to come to grips with Kay's desertion, and it still hurt far worse than he liked to admit.

"Have a seat, Sam," Liana told him. "I'll fix some coffee."

"You don't have to do that, Liana. I don't want to interrupt anything."

"You aren't interrupting anything," Liana responded. "Besides, Neal wants to ask a favor of you."

"Oh?" Sam murmured warily as he slid into the booth across from Neal. "What kind of a favor?"

Neal chuckled. "You can relax, Sam. This favor is simple and painless. Liana's trying to buy my photo finishing store, and we need to close the deal before I leave. In order for the bank to process her loan in time, she needs a contract from you to verify her financial status. Will you give her one?"

"Sure," Sam said as he looked over at Liana. So that's why she'd needed the money so badly that she'd taken his job. At least one piece of the puzzle regarding her had just fallen into place. He wished the rest of the pieces would be so cooperative. "I'll have my secretary draw one up tomorrow. Would it help if I gave you half the money in advance?"

Liana's eyes widened in surprise at the generous offer. "As a matter of fact, it would."

"Then I'll have my secretary draw up a check, too."

"You're being so understanding about this that I hate to ask one more favor, but I need a day off so I can get all the paperwork to the bank," she told him.

"That's no problem," Sam said. "In fact, I could use a day to catch up on things at the office. We'll pick the contract up on our way home tomorrow evening and you can take it to the bank the next day."

"Well, now that that's settled, I've got to run," Neal said as he rose and walked across the room to Liana. He gave her a hug and a quick peck on the cheek. "See you later, sweetheart, and thanks for taking on the ladies." He gave Sam a wave as he walked toward the door. "Take care, Sam, and thanks for the help."

"Anytime," Sam replied, transferring his gaze to Liana the moment Neal was gone. Neal's use of the endearment "sweetheart" had him convinced that his earlier assumption was right. Liana was in love with Neal and he was walking out on her. Sam knew he should be feeling sympathy for her, but instead he was experiencing an odd twinge of irritation. It took a moment for him to realize that it was because he didn't like the thought of Liana being in love with Neal. He didn't like it at all.

"What ladies are you taking on?" he asked.

"African violets," Liana stated dryly as she brought his coffee to him and sat down.

"African violets?" Sam repeated in confusion.

Liana nodded. "I've been given the dubious honor of inheriting Neal's African violets, whom he calls his ladies."

"I see," Sam said. He leaned back in the booth and studied her face, trying to assess her mood. If she was upset, she wasn't showing it, but then again, he thought with chagrin, she rarely showed any emotion. "How long have you known Neal?"

"Ten—no, eleven years," she answered. "We met when I was in college. He was a guest lecturer for one of my photography classes, and we'd been asked to bring what we considered a newsworthy photograph to class for him to critique. He was so impressed with my photo of homeless people waiting in a soup line that he offered me a job as his summer protégèe."

She sipped her tea before continuing, "That summer was a major turning point in my life. I had always wanted to be a newspaper photojournalist, but Neal discovered this very big flaw in my personality."

"What kind of flaw?" Sam prodded when she drifted off into thoughtful silence.

"I empathize with my subjects too closely, and there is so much tragedy to record in the newspaper business that I was perpetually depressed," she replied. "Neal was certain that if I stayed in the field, it would destroy my creative talent, so he put me in touch with a group of free-lance photographers who did everything from advertaising shots to *National Georgraphic* layouts.

"I still had my share of tragic subjects over the years, but after I finished my apprenticeship, I had control over my assignments, so I was able to keep them at a minimum. At the time I thought Neal had done me a favor, but now..."

"But now?" Sam encouraged when she once again drifted off into silence. When she didn't answer, he reached across the table and caught her hand. "Liana?"

She shook her head, as if pulling herself from somewhere faraway. "I'm sorry, Sam. I shouldn't be sitting here boring you with my past."

"You aren't boring me," Sam murmured, taking note of the bright sheen of tears in her eyes. "Are you okay?"

"Of course," Liana answered with forced cheerfulness. "Let me get the photographs for your grandfather. I hate to brag, but some of them are really spectacular."

Before Sam could respond, she left the room, and he frowned down at his coffee, feeling more confused than ever. As he'd listened to her talk about Neal, he'd gotten the distinct impression that there was nothing romantic between them, which meant that whatever was troubling her was not an affair of the heart. Gut instinct told him that whatever it was was linked to that unfinished sentence. *At the time I thought Neal had done me a favor, but now...*

But now, what? Sam asked himself in frustration. The obvious conclusion, of course, was that Neal hadn't done her a favor, but how could getting her a job that would protect her from tragedy and perpetual depression not be a favor? It just didn't make any sense.

He decided that the only way he was going to get down to the bottom of the maddening mystery was to ask Liana what was troubling her, and that was exactly what he was going to do the minute she returned.

But when she walked back into the room and handed him the pictures, she was smiling and her eyes were sparkling with anticipatory excitement while she waited for him to look at her work. Sam released an inward sigh of resignation as he shuffled through the pile of photographs, knowing that he'd rather die than bring the tears back to her eyes.

His questions were just going to have to wait, but he knew he couldn't let them wait much longer. His fascination with her was shifting toward infatuation, and he couldn't let that happen. Even though infatuation was nothing more than a temporary bout of insanity, it didn't make a man immune to a broken heart.

As far as Sam was concerned, he'd had enough heartbreak to last him a lifetime, and only a fool would open himself up for more. And he was *not* a fool, he told himself firmly when he glanced up at Liana, as stunned by her beauty now as he had been the first day he'd laid eyes on her.

At that moment, he began to doubt the veracity of his words. Perhaps he was a fool, and he had a sinking feeling that he always would be when it came to this woman.

Chapter Six

"What in the world are you doing?" Sam questioned in disbelief when he walked into his mother's living room and found her sitting in the middle of the floor surrounded by boxes.

Her head shot up in surprise. "Sam! I didn't hear you come in, but I'm glad you're here. You can help me."

Sam arched a brow as his gaze drifted over the boxes and back to his mother. She looked so young with her face smudged with dust and her hair disheveled that he couldn't help but smile at her.

"I'm afraid to hear the answer, but what, exactly, do you want me to do?" he asked as he laid the photographs that he'd got from Liana on the end table.

"I'm cleaning out the attic," she answered. "A lot of this stuff is yours. I need you to go through it and decide what you want to keep and what can be thrown out."

Sam gave a dazed shake of his head. The attic had been his mother's catchall for thirty-five years, and he'd never known her to throw anything away. She was either convinced that an item would be worth money someday or she'd attached sentimental value to it, although he had no idea what monetary or sentimental value a rusty spatula with a broken handle could hold as he took note of the one lying in the open box in front of her.

"What has caused this sudden urge for spring cleaning?" he inquired indulgently.

He was astonished to see her blush a bright crimson at his question, and instead of answering, she held out her left hand. Sam felt the bottom fall out of his stomach. Her ring finger sported a modest diamond engagement ring.

He knew he shouldn't be surprised. After all, Tom had popped the question the first of the year. Then his grandfather had fallen ill and his mother had put Tom off. Suddenly, Sam realized that he'd subconsciously believed her answer would be no.

"Well, say something," his mother said, a catch in her voice.

"Congratulations," he managed around the lump in his throat.

"It is okay with you, isn't it, Sam?"

He would have to be deaf not the hear the worry in her voice, her need for reassurance. He walked to her, helped her to her feet and gave her a hug. "Of course, it's okay with me. I just hope Tom appreciates what a wonderful woman he's getting."

"That works both ways," she said as she stepped away from him and nervously smoothed her skirt. "The reason I'm cleaning out the attic is because I've decided to sell the house. Tom's place is much bigger, and there's plenty of room for Dad. In fact, he'll have a huge bedroom with a southwestern exposure that will give him plenty of sunshine and a gorgeous view of the mountains."

"It sounds...great," Sam responded, trying to sound enthused. But even to him the words sounded flat. His parents had moved into this house when he was a year old, and it had always been home to him, even if he hadn't actually lived in it for more than seventeen years. He'd known that if his mother married Tom there were going to be changes, but he hadn't realized that his entire past was going to be wiped out in the blink of an eye. What would he have to hold on to if he couldn't hold on to his childhood memories?

It was hard, but he asked, "So, when's the big day?"

"We haven't set one yet, but sometime in June." She blushed again and glanced shyly at her feet. "I've always wanted to be a June bride."

"I know," Sam murmured. "I remember how Dad used to say that someday he was going to make an honest woman out of you by trading in your marriage licence from the justice of the peace and throwing you a humdinger of a June wedding."

Abigail nodded, brushing her hair away from her face. "I've been thinking about your father a lot lately. I suppose I had to come to some sort of peace with him before I could accept Tom, but it's been hard, Sam. In the last few months I've realized how angry I've been with him for abandoning us like that. The worst part is, I'm still angry with him. If he'd just left us a note to tell us why he felt he had to take his own life, I think I could have dealt with it. Why didn't he leave us a note, Sam?"

Sam could only shake his head when she glanced up at him plaintively, seeking answers he couldn't give. Her question also brought forth a rush of pain, pain as intense as it had been twenty years before. It was then that he understood that he, too, was angry with his father, and would most likely be so for the remainder of his life. As his mother said, if his father had left a note telling them why he'd killed himself, maybe they could have dealt with it. It would have also confirmed or denied the guilt that rode on Sam's shoulders—the guilt that insisted his father's suicide had been his fault, that he could have prevented it if he'd only taken one small step.

But his guilt had no place in this moment in time. His mother had just taken a large step toward the future—a step that had been too long in coming—and he wanted to pull her away from the past. He took her hand and led her to the boxes.

"Now, where should I begin?" he asked with forced enthusiasm as he rolled up his shirt sleeves.

Abigail sat down on the floor and laughed softly, almost girlishly, as she pushed a box toward him. "I guess we'll just have to take it one box at a time."

Sam had known the project was going to be difficult, but he hadn't realized how difficult until he ripped open the top of the box and found himself staring at the last snapshot that had been taken of him and his father.

LIANA CAST A SURREPTITIOUS LOOK at Sam as he opened the back of the car to get their packs. He'd been uncommunicative during the hour and a half drive into the mountains, and she knew that something was wrong. Unfortunately, she didn't know how to approach him without seeming to pry.

"Sam?" she tentatively inquired as he hauled their packs out of the back of the car.

"Yeah?" he responded tersely, refusing to look at her.

Liana stuffed her hands into her jacket pockets and frowned. If he wanted to act like a brick wall, that was okay with her. But he could at least have the courtesy to face her when she was talking to him.

"Is something wrong?" she asked, deciding that if he took her concern as prying so be it.

"No," he answered as he slammed the window closed with more force than necessary. "Why?"

"You're awfully quiet today."

"I've got a lot on my mind," he stated as he thrust her pack at her.

She took her pack and slipped it on. "Well, if you'd like to talk about whatever is bothering you, I—"

"I don't want to talk," Sam interrupted curtly. "If I did, I'd be talking."

"Fine," Liana responded stiffly. "Forgive me for being so rude as to think you might need a friendly ear."

With that, she turned on her heel and walked toward the nearby trail.

Sam ground his teeth in frustration as he watched her traverse the steep slope with sure-footed confidence. He couldn't believe he'd been so rude to her, and he muttered a litany of expletives as he shrugged on his pack. He owed her an apology and he knew it, but what was he supposed to say? *I spent several torturous hours reliving a painful past last night, and I had to pretend it didn't bother me so I wouldn't upset my mother?*

By the time he caught up with her, he still hadn't figured out how to apologize, and he almost ran into her when she stopped abruptly.

She glanced over her shoulder at him as she began to shed her pack, and in a tone that brooked no argument, she whispered, "I want you to stay right where you are. Don't move a muscle. Don't even breathe. I mean it, Sam."

Before Sam could assimilate the order, Liana had eased her pack to the ground and crept stealthily into the brush. He watched her progress, and after determining her direction, raised his eyes and searched the area, trying to discover what had attracted her attention.

Although Sam knew that Liana's order not to breathe had been figurative, he literally couldn't breathe when his gaze finally landed on the huge mountain lion crouched on the ridge above them. The animal was awe-inspiring. He also looked dangerous as hell.

Sam quickly transferred his attention to the brush, searching for Liana who'd disappeared from sight. When she reappeared in a small clearing, his heart pounded in fear for her safety. She was so close to the animal that it looked as if she could reach out and touch him.

Sam was torn between the urge to go after her and risk scaring off the big cat or staying in place as she'd instructed. *She's done this before. She knows what she's doing,* he told himself.

But he'd no more than formulated the thought than the mountain lion growled and leaped from the ridge, heading directly for Liana.

With an explosive curse, Sam tore through the underbrush, certain the animal was after her and hoping he'd be able to distract it so she'd have a chance to escape. He cursed again when his pack caught on a scrub oak, and he heaved himself away from the tenacious plant, taking half of it with him.

His breathing was harsh, labored, when he finally broke into the small clearing where he'd last seen Liana, and his fear coalesced into a rage when he saw her standing there looking as if she didn't have a care in the world.

He ran toward her, ready to shake the stuffing right out of her for putting herself into such a life-threatening position and scaring the daylights out of him. But when he reached her, Liana spun around to face him with excited laughter. Before he could catch his breath to yell at her, she threw her arms around his neck and exclaimed, "Wasn't he the most magnificent creature you've ever seen?"

Sam automatically linked his arms around her waist to steady them, and his anger evaporated as he stared down at her, deciding that nothing in the world could be more magnificent than Liana. The full impact of her beauty, enhanced with sparkling eyes and a brilliant smile, was breathtaking. Sam reacted on instinct and instinct alone. He lowered his head and kissed her.

Liana was so caught off-guard by Sam's kiss that she didn't even attempt to pull away. As his lips brushed hers, entreating and tempting with their feather-light caress, her own lips began to ache for more. She wrapped her arms securely around his neck and leaned into him so she could communicate her need.

With a groan, Sam tightened his hold around her and drew her close, obeying her silent appeal by deepening the kiss. Liana's head began to spin when she felt the urgent flick of his tongue, his insistent demand for entrance into her mouth. She instinctually complied and was rewarded by Sam's low growl of approval as his tongue explored her with a sweet, tormenting tenderness that caused tears to sting her eyes.

She was so caught up in the sensation of simply feeling— of acknowledging nothing more than the delicious press of Sam's mouth—that she released a whimper of disapproval when he began to ease away from the kiss. Then he released her completely and moved away, leaving her feeling disoriented, much like she'd once felt when she'd been lost in a heavy fog.

Sam's voice was ragged when he said, "I suppose I should apologize for kissing you, but I'm not going to, because I'm not sorry."

Liana slowly raised her head, and when she met his gaze, her knees began to tremble and her palms grew damp. His eyes were dark with a primitive glow. His nostrils were flared slightly, and he flicked his tongue across his bottom lip, communicating a primal hunger that struck a responding chord in Liana.

The sensation was so unexpected that her first impulse was to run, but something held her in place. Perhaps it was the look in Sam's eyes that told her he expected her to do just that. Perhaps it was that she was tired of running. It was an odd time and place for the revelation to hit home, but she suddenly understood that that's what she'd been doing for the past three years—running as fast as she could, but unable to put any distance between herself and the past.

"It's okay," she told him, refusing to let her mind go any further than that simple acknowledgement. Revelations should be explored in privacy. "Just don't let it happen again."

As she walked back toward the trail, Sam's eyes followed her. When she disappeared into the brush, his lips curved into a ironic smile. *Just don't let it happen again,* she'd said. He agreed with her in principle, so why did he feel as if that kiss had just been the beginning?

Liana was having similar thoughts by the time they stopped for lunch. They hadn't spoken a word since she'd walked away from him, and as they settled down to eat, the silence between them was so palpable that it fairly crackled.

Liana shifted uncomfortably as Sam's words following that kiss reverberated in her ears. *I suppose I should apologize for kissing you, but I'm not going to, because I'm not sorry.*

She knew that she should be sorry, but; oddly enough, she wasn't. That worried her, because today she'd discovered that she was terribly attracted to Sam. She didn't know why she found that surprising. After all, if he walked down the street, three-quarters of the women on it would turn around for a second look.

But Liana knew that it wasn't the outside package she found so compelling. It was his green eyes that shifted through a thousand different moods, sometimes so swiftly she couldn't keep up with them. It was his deep-timbered voice that vibrated with love as he talked about his grandfather. It was his devil-may-care grin that appeared after a treacherous climb up a cliff. It was his strong yet gentle hands that lowered a flea-ridden cat into a bathtub.

Sam touched her on an emotional level, and she knew that was dangerous. A simple physical attraction could be easily handled, but when the heart started getting involved, everything became very complicated. If she wasn't careful, she'd find herself falling in love, and love was not a condition that she could afford. Thankfully she would be going to the bank tomorrow, so she wouldn't be seeing Sam. She needed those twenty-four hours away from him so she could bolster up her defenses.

"What did you say?" she asked, jerked away from her troubling thoughts when she realized Sam had spoken.

"I said I owe you an apology for being so rude this morning. I shouldn't have snapped at you when you offered a friendly ear."

"It's okay. We all have bad days," she said with a dismissive shrug. She'd forgotten all about that little scene at the foot of the mountain.

"That's no excuse for rudeness." He leaned back on the boulder he was sitting on and rested his weight on his forearms. "You've never talked about your parents. Are they still alive?"

"Yes," Liana answered, uncomfortable with the direction his conversation was taking. Because of her self-imposed exile from her parents, she didn't want to discuss them, particularly when she thought about her mother's postcards and that nagging little suspicion that something was wrong.

"Are they still married, or are they one of the statistics of divorce?" he asked next.

"They'll have been married thirty-five years next month," Liana answered, experiencing a pang of wistful longing. She wondered if her parents would have an anniversary party to celebrate that milestone in their marriage. She hoped so. Her mother so loved a good party.

"My mother's been a widow for twenty years, and yesterday she got engaged," Sam announced.

"And how do you feel about that?" Liana inquired as she pulled her knees up to her chest and looped her arms around them.

"I can't decide," Sam said as he gave her a perplexed look. "One part of me is very happy for her. Tom is a good man, and he adores my mother. But there's another part of me that feels betrayed. Pretty childish, huh?"

"It sounds pretty human to me, Sam. If something happened to one of my parents and the other decided to remarry, I think I'd feel torn. Let's face it, you have an image of your parents in your mind, and that image says they belong together. You're being asked to superimpose another man over your father in that picture."

"This has nothing to do with my father. He gave up his rights to that picture a long time ago," Sam stated tightly as he shot up off the boulder and grabbed his pack off the ground. "We've wasted enough time. If we're going to get back to the car before dark, we'd better get going."

Liana stared at him in wide-eyed surprise. She'd definitely trod on a very tender subject this time, but what had he meant when he said his father had given up his rights to that picture a long time ago? He'd told her that his father had died when he was sixteen. Had his parents been divorced? But that didn't make any sense, because if they had been, his mother wouldn't be a widow. Or had she lost a second husband. All the questions were too complicated, and since it was apparent that Sam was not in the mood to give her any answers, Liana shrugged them off.

Besides, she told herself as she followed him down the mountain, the less she knew about him, the better off she'd be. He'd already gotten too close, and she wasn't about to let him get any closer.

But despite her resolve, she found herself filled with longing as they passed the spot where they'd shared that steamy kiss, and Liana had the deep suspicion that twenty-four hours wouldn't be nearly enough time to shore up her defenses against him. In fact, she suspected that twenty-four years wouldn't be long enough.

SAM ARCHED AN APPRAISING BROW when they pulled up in front of his office to get Liana's contract and check.

"Either Margaret forgot to turn off the lights or trouble's brewing," he said as he climbed out of the car.

"Do you want me to wait here?" Liana asked while she eyed his place of business. It was an old Victorian house which, like so many old homes that lined major thoroughfares in cities across the country, had become an undesirable family dwelling because of the incessant traffic.

She glanced up and down the street, noting that a business shingle hung from a post in nearly every yard, and even though the exteriors of the turn-of-the-century residences were impeccably maintained, Liana couldn't help but wonder if the houses mourned the loss of children scampering across their floors, of not being showered with the love of a family.

She shook her head, dismissing her whimsy, when Sam opened her door and said, "No, I don't want you to wait out here. There couldn't possibly be anything going on that you can't be privy to."

"You're sure?" she inquired hesitantly. "I really don't mind waiting."

"Liana, please come in," Sam said, a tinge of impatience in his voice. "It's probably Pat, and she's probably waiting to give me an earful."

"Who's Pat?" Liana asked as she climbed out and walked with him toward the door.

"My foreman."

As they reached the door, it flew open to reveal a tall, slender blonde.

"It's about time you got here," the woman grumbled at Sam. "Swenson is going to drive me crazy."

"Good evening to you, too," Sam said, grabbing Liana's arm and leading her inside. "Pat, this is Liana Stevens. Liana, this is Pat Williams."

Liana knew she was staring, but she couldn't help herself. Pat Williams was so gorgeous she should be on the front page of magazines, not scrambling around rooftops!

"Glad to meet you," Pat told her.

"The same," Liana managed to mumble as they shook hands.

Sam took her arm again and led her down a short hallway. They entered a large room that had been converted into an office. Papers were piled high on a gigantic antique oak desk. Sam lifted a stack of files out of a matching oak chair and gave it a quick dusting before gesturing to Liana. She took the offered seat.

"So what's up with Swenson?" he asked while Pat grabbed a stack of files from the remaining chair and handed them to him. He dropped both piles onto the only blank spot on his desk.

Pat collapsed into her chair and frowned petulantly. "He's a male chauvinist boor."

Sam leaned one hip against the desk, curled his hands around the edge and crossed his ankles. "I told you that before we took the job, but you said you could handle him."

"I know," Pat muttered. "But he isn't responding to any of my techniques, and he's trying to undermine my authority, Sam. He actually climbed up on the roof and started ordering my crew around. When I tried to talk to him, he told me that the only person more stupid than a broad who wants a man's job was a man foolish enough to hire her in the first place. I'm telling you, I almost pushed him off the roof, and it was four stories down."

Sam chuckled, and when Pat sent him a murderous glare in response, he gave her an unrepentant smile as he leaned forward and gave her shoulder a comforting squeeze. "I'm sure you handled him beautifully."

She rolled her eyes dramatically. "I'm serious, Sam. I'm about ready to murder the man, and it would be justifiable homicide."

"Well, I'm going to be in the office tomorrow, so I'll drop by the site and have a talk with him. I'll let him know that if he keeps hassling you, we'll walk off the job."

"Thanks, Sam. I really appreciate it."

"No problem. Good foremen are hard to find," Sam said, smiling at her fondly.

"So are good bosses," she replied, smiling back.

Liana glanced between them, and noting their shared look that smacked of intimacy, felt a twinge of something that felt suspiciously like jealousy. Refusing to acknowledge, let alone even contemplate, that twinge, she mentally shoved the notion aside and looked around the room as they discussed other business.

The bottom half of the walls was a wainscoting of dark oak paneling. The upper half was a tasteful striped wallpaper of yellow, gold and brown, which made the room pleasantly masculine but not overwhelmingly so. He had a grouping of photographs on the wall nearest to her, which she scanned briefly before homing in on a black-and-white snapshot of a much younger Sam and an older man. Their pose, arms linked around one another's shoulders and their smiles wide, proclaimed their closeness, and although there wasn't even a vague physical resemblance between them, Liana knew instinctively that the older man was Sam's grandfather.

She studied the man with intense interest as she recalled his philosophy about the seasons of a man's years. At first he appeared too roughhewn to be a man capable of such deep thought. But on closer scrutiny, she could see the philosopher imprinted in the character lines of his face and in the intelligent gleam of his eyes.

"I was twenty-four when that picture was taken. I'd just landed my first big roofing contract and Gramps threw me a party to celebrate."

Startled by Sam's voice, which seemed to be hovering next to her ear, Liana snapped her head around and discovered that Sam had squatted down beside her chair. She glanced beyond him, surprised to see that she'd been so absorbed with the photograph that she hadn't heard Pat leave.

She returned her attention to Sam and was disquieted by his expression. He was staring at the picture broodingly, and there was a sardonic tilt to his lips that put the entire scene askew in her mind. He adored his grandfather and she knew it, so why would he look at the picture like that?

Before she had a chance to figure out what was going on, he stood. "I'd better find your contract and your check."

Liana nodded and searched his face, trying to latch onto his elusive mood. But his face was studiously closed, invincible to her probing.

He dug through the papers on his desk while grumbling, "You know, I've come to the conclusion that paperwork breeds like rabbits. Put two pieces of paper together and you have twenty before morning. Ah, here's what you need!" He handed her some papers and a pen. "If it looks okay, sign both copies."

Liana skimmed over the contract, deciding that it was cut and dried. She signed both copies and handed them back to him. He scrawled his signature across the bottom of the papers, gave her one copy and a check, and tossed the additional copy onto a nearby pile.

"Are you hungry?" he asked, his smile casual, yet emoting a sense of frenzy that Liana didn't understand. Intuition told her that whatever it was had to do with the photograph of him and his grandfather, and she resisted the urge to look back at the picture. Once again she tried to latch onto his mood, but remained unsuccessful. The fact that she couldn't read him was disconcerting, because she was invariably able to identify with what a person was feeling if she put her mind to it.

"Actually, I am hungry," she said in answer to his question.

"Then you'll have dinner with me? I hate to eat alone. It's so—alone."

Liana's heart lurched at his guileless admission of loneliness and every self-protective instinct inside her told her to refuse the invitation. He was already too close, she reminded herself. She couldn't let him get any closer. She had to say no. But when she met his gaze which was filled with hopeful expectancy, she couldn't bring herself to do it.

This is dangerous, her conscience observed dolefully. She nodded in acknowledgement of the internal warning, aware that Sam was taking her nod as an agreement to his dinner invitation. She didn't correct his assumption, even though she had the distinct feeling that she'd just made one of the worst mistakes of her life.

Chapter Seven

"So, where would you like to eat?" Sam asked as they walked to the car.

Liana looked at him and then down at herself. "We're so dusty that a decent restaurant wouldn't let us in the door. Do you like hamburgers?"

"Have you met a red-blooded man who doesn't?"

"No. Is there a Stevens around here?" she asked, naming a fast-food hamburger conglomerate that had started on the East coast several years before and had spread through the West like brushfire during the last decade.

"Right down the street."

"Good. Let's eat there."

"That's fine with me," Sam said, although he would have preferred a nice, dark restaurant. It wasn't intimacy he craved as much as a means to hide his agitation.

When he'd looked at the old snapshot of him and his grandfather, he'd realized that twelve years had gone by since that momentous day and he had very little to show for the passage of time. Oh, he was successful in business, but his personal life had bottomed out. He no longer had a wife. He didn't have any children. Hell, he didn't even have a goldfish to share his success with.

He wasn't normally disposed toward despondent moods, but, as had been occurring more and more frequently since his grandfather's debilitating illness, depression descended upon him and he couldn't seem to shake it off. The fact that he couldn't frightened him, because his father had been a victim of extreme bouts of depression, and the old axiom of, "Like father, like son," kept echoing through his mind. He couldn't help but wonder if he was destined to come to the same tragic end. Was suicide an inherited disorder?

He drove to the hamburger joint in silence, worrying at the problem all the way. As far as he was concerned, suicide was a weak man's way out and he'd never considered himself weak. But then again, he'd never considered his father weak, either, and look what had happend. To add fuel to the fire, his father had been exactly his age when he'd chosen to take his life, and that reminder sent a shiver of apprehension racing down Sam's spine. He felt as if he'd just received some type of omen, and he sighed in relief when he spotted Stevens and pulled into the parking lot. Suddenly, bright lights were very appealing and he hurried Liana inside.

After receiving their orders of hamburgers and fries and settling into a booth near the door, Liana took a big bite out of her hamburger.

She released a satisfied sigh and said, "I'm always amazed that every Stevens hamburger I eat tastes as good as the first one I had. Of course, my taste buds are probably prejudiced by family allegiance."

"Family allegiance?" Sam repeated in confusion.

"Yes." She nibbled on a fresh fry before saying, "Stevens is owned by my family. I told you that my grandparents had gone into fast food."

Sam nearly choked on the hamburger. When she'd told him her grandparents had gone into fast food, he hadn't realized that they'd *gone* into fast food. That made her an heiress, didn't it? But if that was true, why was she struggling to get enough money together for a bank loan?

Seemingly unaware that her announcement had been startling. Liana continued, "I was just a baby when the first Stevens opened, but according to my father, my grandparents, after thirty-seven years of wedded bliss, had their first knock-down, drag-out fight over it. Grandfather felt that fast food meant just that. You got in quick and you got out fast, so why should he spend any money on interior decorating? He figured a few cheap tables and chairs were more than sufficient for those people who wanted to eat inside rather than take their food with them.

"Grandmother, however, objected strenuously. She felt that anyone with enough good sense to sit down to eat their meal should have their digestive tract aided by a comfortable atmosphere. She finally resorted to a wife's oldest trick to get her way."

Sam grinned when Liana gave him a conspiratorial wink and took another bite of her hamburger. Knowing she was waiting for him to ask the obvious, he complied. "She stopped sleeping with him?"

Liana took her time chewing and swallowing her food, drawing out the anticipation. Finally, she responded, "Nope. She nagged him to death."

She was pleased when Sam burst into laughter, dispelling his glum mood. She also decided that she liked his laugh. It was rich and hearty and as vibrant as he was.

When he recovered, he said, "Thanks, Liana. I needed that."

She gave a shy nod and concentrated on her food. She wanted to ask why he'd suddenly sunk into such a black funk at his office, but she knew that the question would be a step toward intimacy she wasn't willing to take. She had to maintain her distance.

Instead, she said, "Pat is a gorgeous woman. I was flabbergasted when you told me she was your foreman. Are there many women in the business?"

"More than you'd think," Sam replied. "However, it'll be several years before the roofers of America need to worry about a feminist takeover."

"You're against feminism?" Liana asked, surprised by his words, especialy after the conversation he'd had with Pat. Was he just another man who talked a good game, but actually felt very differently about the issue? The thought that he might be filled her with disappointment.

"I'm against any 'ism' that labels a group of people and makes them targets for prejudice by the very nature of their existence," Sam replied. "I prefer to function on the precept that every person is an individual and should be evaluated as such."

"That's exactly what feminism is all about," Liana pointed out, relieved by his answer. "I agree that there should be no need for people to band together to ensure they're treated fairly. Unfortunately, that's still a utopian dream. Despite the great strides that have been made in our society, there are still a good number of men who refuse to accept women as their equals."

There was a teasing glint in Sam's eyes when he said, "But women are not equal to men."

Liana stiffened indignantly in her seat. "You can't be saying that men are superior to women!"

"No. I'm saying that women are superior to men."

He grinned as he continued, "I've met a lot of women who hold down a full-time job, raise a family and keep an immaculate house. In the two years I've been divorced, I have yet to figure out how to do my laundry without turning my underwear into shades of pastel that would get me drummed out of my health club, and without my housekeeper, the city health department would condemn my apartment. Heaven only knows what I'd be like if I also had a couple of kids to contend with, not to mention a significant other, as Pat is so fond of saying, demanding their fair share of my time. I don't have the inborn organizational skills that most women seem to be blessed with."

"Those skills aren't inborn, they're learned," Liana stated. "Before I moved to Denver, my apartment was in shambles, I couldn't have organized a fire drill, and if you'd given me a couple of kids to raise, I'd have had a nervous breakdown before noon."

"And now?" Sam asked quietly.

Liana swallowed hard as she met his eyes, which were dark with what she would have sworn was a sensual gleam, causing a not unpleasant tingling in the small of her back. "And now what?"

"Do you feel competent to do all of those things?"

"Well, everything but the kids. I've never been very good with kids."

Sam smiled. "I find that hard to believe. If I remember correctly, some of your award-winning photographs were of children."

The heating vent for the building was directly over her head, but Liana shivered as her mind provided her with one of those perennial flashes from the past. She could hear children screaming. See their mouths widened in terror. And then there was the blood. Everywhere she looked, there was the blood.

She fought against the bile rising in her throat and forced herself back to the present. Realizing that Sam was watching her through narrowed eyes, she knew it was time to divert the conversation.

"Why did the picture of you and your grandfather make you so sad?" she asked, deciding that it was better to take that step toward intimacy with him than have him quizzing her.

Sam knew she was purposely changing the subject, and he was filled with a sense of growing frustration. Every time they began to approach any subject that would give him some personal insight into her, she withdrew or turned the conversation back on him. Why was she so reluctant to talk about herself?

He finished off his hamburger and his fries while trying to decide if he wanted to answer her question. One part of him said that he shouldn't tell her any more than she was willing to tell him, and that was close to nothing. But the other part said that if he confided in her, perhaps she'd gain enough trust in him to share her confidences.

He ripped open the paper package that contained the straw for his soft drink, but instead of putting it into his drink he began to idly toy with it while he tried to reach a decision.

Finally, he said, "When I looked at that photograph, I realized that twelve years of my life have gone by and I really have nothing to show for it."

"How can you say that?" Liana asked, surprised by his answer. "You own your own business, and you told me yourself that you're successful. There are a lot of people who'd love to be able to make that claim."

"Maybe," Sam replied. "But one of my main objectives for becoming a success was to provide an easy life for my wife. Just as I reached that pinnacle, she walked out without a good-bye or a drop dead. Now I'm sitting here with money to burn and no one to burn it on. Considering that, can you honestly say all my effort was worth it?"

"Of course it was," Liana stated with conviction. "Just because your ex-wife didn't appreciate you and what you've accomplished doesn't mean some other woman won't. You need to put the past behind you, Sam, and move forward."

He gave her a rueful smile as he softly asked, "Are you ready to follow your own advice, Liana?"

The question hit Liana with the force of a blow, and she glanced down at the hamburger in her hand. She'd walked right into that one with both eyes open. "Our circumstances are not the same."

"How are they different?"

"I can't tell you that."

"Can't or won't?"

"Both," Liana answered as she glanced back up at him with a disconcerted frown. It suddenly dawned on her that she was always ducking his questions, but she could stop them completely by giving him a measure of truth. "Even if I wanted to tell you about my circumstances, I couldn't. My past is a matter of national security, and I'm not allowed to discuss it."

Sam was so stunned by her answer that he gaped at her. How in the world could a freelance photographer's past be a matter of national security? He was flooded with a million questions, but he suddenly realized that if what she claimed was true, he'd be wasting his breath asking them, because she couldn't give him the answers.

Disconcerted by the situation, Sam raked a hand through his hair and said, "You'd better finish your hamburger."

Liana bit into her hamburger, but it was now tasteless, and she found her attention centered on Sam's hands as he began to once again toy with his straw. She watched, mesmerized, as he idly stroked the narrow plastic tube and, unbidden, an image of his hands touching her in intimacy rose in her mind.

Liana closed her eyes to make the image go away. She couldn't allow herself even to contemplate such a fantasy, because it could never come to fruition. With a sigh, she opened her eyes and wrapped the remainder of her hamburger back in the paper.

When Sam eyed her efforts questioningly, she said, "It's a bribe for Hooligan. I'll trade him half a Stevens burger for an uninterrupted night of sleep."

"I'll look forward to finding out if he can be bribed," Sam said as he stood and helped her into her coat, raising the collar and smoothing it around her neck.

His actions were completely asexual, like a parent preparing a child to go out and face the cold, and, perhaps, that was exactly why all of Liana's insides went weak. It was also then that she understood how truly dangerous Sam was.

Since she'd met him, he'd made her feel, and though she'd prefer not to, she knew she could live with that. But that one undemanding, caring gesture had been like a gentle rainfall on her parched soul, and, heaven help her, it had given life to need.

Need was something Liana couldn't live with, and she hurried out to Sam's car without even waiting to see if he was following. She wanted to get as far away from him as possible. She *had* to get away from him before it was too late.

But when he joined her and unlocked the passenger door, Liana knew that she could travel to the other side of the world and she wouldn't be able to escape him. As unbelievable as it seemed, by simply raising the collar of her coat, Sam had stolen a tiny little piece of her heart. If she'd been capable of shedding tears, she would have sat down and cried.

SAM TUCKED HIS HANDS INTO HIS BACK POCKETS as he walked Liana to her door. It was the only way he could keep them from reaching out for her. The problem was he didn't know if he wanted to shake her out of frustration or to hold her close and comfort her.

Her revelation at Stevens had left him reeling, and the more he thought about it, the more he began to doubt the validity of her words. He didn't think she was actually lying to him, but he felt that she could probably reveal far more than she was letting on.

When they reached the front door, Sam said, "I hope everything goes well at the bank tomorrow."

"Thanks." Liana walked up the steps and unlocked the front door. But even as she curled her hand around the doorknob, she knew she wasn't ready to let Sam go. It was crazy, insane and even out-and-out demented, but she found herself asking, "Would you like to come in for coffee?"

Sam knew that to accept her offer was not only nuts, but absolutely mad. "I'd love to."

When he walked into her house a moment later, he stared in disbelief. He knew that Neal had given Liana his plants, but he hadn't known what a difference a few plants could make in a room. It was no longer a mausoleum, and even though he didn't feel as if he'd want to fling himself down on the sofa and put his feet up on the coffee table, the room was inviting.

Liana opened the entry closet and pulled out a hanger. Sam shed his down vest and handed it to her. Then he grinned at Hooligan, who wandered into the room, plopped down on his rump and regarded them with a miffed arrogance that succinctly communicated his disapproval at being left alone for the entire day and part of the night.

"I don't think Hooligan appreciates the value of time alone," he said.

"I don't think Hooligan appreciates anything, particularly the hand that feeds him," Liana grumbled as she closed the closet door and automatically reached down to scratch the animal's head.

"I think he does appreciate that," Sam rebutted as the cat fell into step beside her when she walked toward the kitchen. "If he didn't, he would have been waiting at the front door in anticipaton of making his great escape. Instead, he waited until we were inside with the door safely closed behind us before making an appearance."

Liana glanced down at the cat in thoughtful contemplation. Sam was right. Hooligan only showed up when the door was securely shut. The realization that the animal might be afraid of being ousted made her feel guilty for the times she'd lost her temper and threatened him with eviction. She was glad she'd brought home the hamburger as a treat. It would also serve as a peace offering.

Sam settled into the booth and watched Liana break up the remainder of her hamburger onto a plate and set it on the floor for Hooligan. When she pulled the coffeemaker out of the cupboard, his eyes wandered around the room, taking note of even more African violets.

"It's great about Neal's new job, isn't it?" Sam said, wanting her to give him some feedback on her feelings about Neal's departure. Even though he'd already reached the conclusion that there was nothing between them, he needed to have it confirmed.

"Yes, it is great. For as long as I've known him he's wanted to move back to England."

"I know," Sam said with a chuckle. "When we were in high school that's all he talked about, and he used to spend hours practicing his English accent. He said he didn't want to disgrace himself when he went home by developing a

Western twang. I never could find the heart to tell him that he'd already developed one."

Liana had to swallow hard against the sudden lump in her throat at his artless confession. Even as a teenager, Sam had been kind. How many men could make that claim? She felt another tiny little piece of her heart being stolen away and, oddly enough, she felt an inexplicable surge of anger toward his ex-wife. How could the woman have treated him so callously?

"Do you still love your ex-wife?" The words came out before Liana even knew she was thinking them, and she gasped in horror when she realized what she'd said. She wanted to crawl into a hole and die when she saw Sam's shocked expression. "I'm sorry, Sam. That's none of my business."

Sam was too stunned by the deeply personal question that had come from out of nowhere to answer.

A tense silence filled the room as Liana set the tea kettle on the stove for her tea and then made Sam's cup of coffee. The tea kettle began to whistle at the same time that the coffeemaker finished its cycle.

"I'll get my coffee," Sam said. "Go ahead and make your tea."

Liana nodded, still too embarrassed to speak. She also learned how small her cooking area was when Sam joined her and their shoulders bumped as they performed their chores. The unexpected contact caused that pleasant tingling sensation to return to her lower back, and Liana muttered a silent curse when it began to radiate south, intent on proving that, like it or not, she still had a healthy libido. She released an inward sigh of relief when Sam returned to the booth, and she purposely took twice as long to brew her tea.

By the time she sat down, she had herself fairly well under control, but not well enough that she could look at him directly. That's why she jumped when Sam said, "I suppose I do."

"Excuse me?" Liana said, looking at him in confusion.

"I suppose I still love my ex-wife in that I care enough about her to want her to be healthy and happy. But if she knocked on my door tomorrow and asked to come back, I'd have to say no."

"You sound surprised by that fact," Liana commented as she watched a bemused gleam enter his eyes.

"I am surprised," he said. "Not because I'd say no if she asked to come back, but because I just realized that my refusal wouldn't be an act of self-preservation. I'd be doing it because I no longer have husbandly feelings for her, and I don't think I ever could again."

Liana felt a strange sense of relief flood through her at his words. Before she could contemplate the unexpected emotion, her doorbell rang.

"Are you expecting someone?" Sam asked.

Liana frowned and shook her head.

"Then let me get it," Sam told her as he stood. "A woman living alone shouldn't answer her door at night."

Liana's frown deepened as she watched him walk toward the living room with a proprietary swagger. A part of her reveled in feeling protected, while another part nagged that she was coasting on thin ice. She couldn't afford to let Sam get under her skin, but it seemed as if every defense she put up he tore down. More and more she was being drawn to him, and she knew that she had to find a way to strengthen her resolve against his many charms. If she didn't, they were both going to get hurt.

But Liana's frown turned to puzzlement when she heard a young woman say, "Oh, my! I thought this was Liana Stevens' house."

The voice sounded terribly familiar, and Liana had already headed for the living room when she heard Sam's response. "It is. May I tell her who's calling?"

"Adriane?" Liana questioned in disbelief as she entered the room at that moment and saw her sister framed in the doorway.

"Liana!" the young woman squealed as she bolted across the room and threw her arms around Liana in an exuberant hug.

"What in the world are you doing here?" Liana asked as she automatically hugged her back.

Adriane pulled away from the embrace, stuffed her hands into her coat pockets and raised her chin in defiance as she announced, "I've run away from home."

"You've what?" Liana gasped.

"You heard me." She pulled a $100 bill out of her pocket and waved it in Liana's face. "Can you break this? I have to pay the cab driver, and he doesn't have enough change."

"I'll take care of the cab," Sam said, curiously studying the two women. As soon as Liana had spoken the girl's name, he'd realized she was her sister, and he wondered why he hadn't realized it the moment he'd laid eyes on her. She was at least ten years younger than Liana. She was also taller and her figure was boyishly slender rather than lusciously curved. But she had the same shimmering dark brown hair, huge brown eyes and delicate features as Liana. Perhaps he hadn't made the connection because Adriane's face had yet to gain the maturity that Liana's had.

"Oh, thank you," Adriane practically gushed as she turned toward him. "I'll pay you back as soon as I can break this hundred. Would you mind bringing in my bags on your way back?"

"Go get your own bags," Liana muttered irritably. "Sam is not a butler."

"Oh, I didn't think he was," Adriane said, her eyes skimming over Sam with interest. "Your taste in men has certainly improved, Liana."

Liana glared and Sam chuckled.

"I'll get your bags," he said, and disappeared out the door.

"He really is gorgeous."

"Yeah. But I'm not interested in your opinion of Sam. I want to know why you're here."

Adriane ignored her as she walked to the center of the living room and looked around. "Good heavens, your taste in men may have improved, but your decorating skills have gone from bad to worse! This is the most boring room I've ever seen, and where in the world have you hidden the television?"

"I don't own a television. Now, stop ignoring me and answer my question. What are you doing here?"

"I told you. I've run away from home, and you know as well as I do that no one in the family would ever think to look for me here. They all think you've gone completely off the deep end, and they'd know it for certain if they could see your kitchen!" she exclaimed as she peeked into the room. "I'm afraid to ask what your guest room looks like, but don't worry. I brought along plenty of posters, so I'll be comfortable."

Liana tapped the top of her hiking boot against the carpet as she experienced the old urge to strangle her sister. It had been an urge that had been present for longer than Liana cared to remember, and it wasn't sibling rivalry, she assured herself. It was just that Adriane was so damn maddening!

"You won't be here long enough to get comfortable. In fact, tomorrow morning, you're putting yourself on a plane and going back home. You're twenty-years old, Adriane, and twenty-year-old women do not run away from home. They deal with their problems in a mature and rational manner."

"Like you did?" the girl challenged as she stripped off her coat and threw it carelessly onto the sofa. "Or is this one of those lectures of do as I say, not as I do? After all, Liana, you haven't exactly been the epitome of the ideal daughter for the last few years, have you?"

"Hang up your coat," Liana ordered, momentarily stymied for an answer and furious that she didn't have one. "I don't have a maid to pick up after you, and I can guarantee that if I have to do it, everything I pick up will go in the trash."

"Lighten up, okay?" Adriane snatched up her coat. "Where am I supposed to hang it?"

Liana turned toward the entryway closet and came to an abrupt halt when she saw Sam leaning against the doorjamb, his arms crossed over his chest and a half-dozen bags piled at his feet. The interested look on his face told her that he'd been standing there listening for quite a long time, and a flush of embarrassment flooded her cheeks.

How much had he heard? she wondered as her mind raced over her and her sister's conversation.

"Oh, there you are," Adriane stated brightly as she walked past Liana and hung her coat in the closet. Then she turned to Sam and extended her hand. "It appears that my sister has forgotten her manners. I'm Adriane Stevens, and you're?"

"Sam. Sam Dillon," Sam answered as he shook the girl's hand.

"Oh, I love your name!" she trilled. "It's so western, isn't it?" Before Sam could respond, she gave him a helpless look that he knew was contrived and asked, "Would you mind terribly carrying my bags into the guest room? They're just so heavy for a little thing like me.''

"Adriane!" Liana stated warningly.

Sam glanced over Adriane's shoulder and winked at Liana. "I'll be happy to play butler if you'll tell me where the guest room is. After all, we wouldn't want your sister to strain anything."

"Particularly her brain," Liana muttered. Then she sighed in resignation and pointed down the hallway. "The guest room's the second door on the right."

"I'll lead the way," Adriane said.

"You'll stay right where you are and start answering some of my questions," Liana corrected. "Sam can find the guest room on his own."

"Your soical graces are positively nonexistent," the girl grumbled.

"And you're as manipulative as ever," Liana grumbled back. "Why did you run away from home?"

"Because, as you said, I'm a twenty-year-old woman, and Mom and Dad refuse to believe that I'm no longer a child. They have my life all mapped out for me, and it isn't the route I want to follow. We hit a crossroads where we couldn't agree on which way to turn, so I packed my bags and left. I figured a little distance would be good for all of us."

"So they do know where you are," Liana stated in relief.

"No," Adriane answered as she walked back to the sofa and threw herself down on it. "You know Mom and Dad. If they knew where I was, they'd show up and start badgering me all over again."

She glanced up at Liana, her eyes bright with tears. "I'm serious. I need some distance, because right now I'm confused. I'm not sure if I'm fighting them to gain my independence, or if I'm fighting them because I really feel I'm right. All I know is that I'm tired of being their baby. I want to grow up, but they just won't let me do it. Please, let me stay here for a few weeks so I can think things out."

Liana closed her eyes and shook her head at the plea. A part of her sympathized with her sister's position, because she'd had her own confrontation with her parents over her efforts to grow up. But she was now old enough to understand that their concern came from the heart, and she knew they'd be frantic with worry if they couldn't find their baby. She also knew that Adriane was right. This was the last place anyone would look for her.

"You can stay under one condition," she finally said. "You have to call Mom and Dad and tell them where you are."

"But they'll come after me!" the girl wailed.

"Not if you tell them exactly what you told me. They will understand, Adriane. They've gone through this with both Sandy and me."

"But what if you're wrong? What if they won't give me the time I need?"

"Then Liana will stand up for you and make them give you the time that you need," Sam said as he walked up behind Liana and laid his hand on her shoulder. "Right?" he murmured when she angled her head so she could look up at him.

Liana frowned at him, knowing that he didn't understand what he was volunteering her for. The last thing she wanted was to see her parents, let alone stand up against them for her little sister!

"Right?" he repeated more softly as he gazed into her eyes.

"Right," Liana finally repeated, knowing that if she didn't, she'd disappoint him, and for some reason, facing her parents was less threatening than facing Sam's disappointment.

"Oh, thank you!" Adriane exclaimed as she bolted up off the sofa and back into Liana's arms, thrusting Liana against Sam's lean frame.

He caught the weight of both of them and then caught his breath at the feel of Liana pressed against him. He knew that he'd remember that moment for the rest of his life.

"Call Mom and Dad, and call them right this minute," Liana instructed, as aware of Sam as he was of her, and wondering if her blood pressure would ever lower. "I mean it, Adriane. If you don't call them, you can't stay. There's a phone in the guest room. I'll trust you to tell them the truth."

"I will," the girl said as she raced down the hallway.

"I wish I was an only child," Liana muttered as she watched the girl disappear.

"No you don't," Sam said as he turned her in his arms and smiled down at her. "She's adorable, and you know it."

"She's a pain in the neck. So why do I have such empathy for her?"

"Because you care," Sam answered as he brushed his knuckles against her cheek.

He wanted to kiss her so badly that his lips ached, but he knew that he couldn't. There was still too much distance between them, too many issues left unresolved. Besides, he had a feeling that once he started kissing her, it would be impossible to let her go.

"I'll see you the day after tomorrow unless you call and tell me that you need another few days off to help Adriane," he said. "And if you need them, Liana, then please take them. Spring isn't going to disappear because of a few days, and even if it did, your sister is more important than a few pictures."

"Thanks," Liana said as she walked him to the door. "But I think we'll be able to keep on schedule. Adriane says she needs to think, and some time alone will force her to do it."

Before Sam could respond, Adriane yelled, "Liana, come and get this *ugly* cat away from me!"

Sam chuckled. "It sounds like Hooligan has just made another friend."

Liana smiled and shook her head. "Goodnight, Sam, and thanks for taking care of the cab and handling Adriane's bags. You really are a nice man."

He gave her a salute as he said, "Hey, I keep telling you that it's a tough job, but somebody's got to do it."

As Liana watched him walk away, she couldn't think of anyone who was more qualified for the job. She also knew that he'd just stolen even more of her heart when he'd placed her sister above his grandfather's photographs. If she wasn't careful, he was soon going to be the sole owner of it.

Chapter Eight

Sam was hot, tired and irritable. He'd spent a restless night grappling with dreams about Liana. Some of them were James Bond scenarios in which she'd kept telling him to go away because this was a matter of national security. Others were strictly X-rated, and he was ruing that insane moment when he'd kissed her.

He'd already been in a bad mood when he'd gone out to the site where Pat was working with her crew, and it seemed as if he'd barely set foot out of his car before he was in a shouting match with Dan Swenson. Pat hadn't been exaggerating when she said the man was a male chauvinist boor, and for the first time in his adult life, Sam had come close to punching someone in the nose. By the time he'd left the site, he was so frustrated he felt like a keg of gunpowder ready to explode, and knowing he had to find an outlet for his anger, he'd decided to join another of his crews, who were putting a new roof on a medical building near his office.

It was one of those rare spring days when the temperature soared to record-breaking heights, and by midday he'd shed his shirt and tied his handkerchief around his head in a makeshift sweatband. He was also getting an inordinate amount of satisfaction in evisioning each nail as Swenson's head and delivering a hard blow as he pounded it in.

He was so absorbed by the fantasy—which was as close as he'd ever come to actual violence since he was a pacifist at heart—that he jumped in surprise when a worker yelled from below, "Hey, Sam, you've got a visitor!"

"That isn't a visitor," one of his men said as he glanced toward the ground and let out a low wolf-whistle. "That's a vision from heaven."

Sam frowned as he crawled to the edge of the building and peered down. At first he didn't recognize the woman gazing up at him, and when he realized it was Liana, he could only stare at her in open-mouthed astonishment. She was wearing a dress and her hip-length hair was hanging free. She looked like Lady Godiva in clothes.

Without realizing what he was doing, he yelled, "Liana? What's wrong? Is it Adriane?"

"Adriane's fine," she yelled back. "Are you going to come down, or are we going to keep caterwauling at each other?"

Sam blushed when several of his men started chuckling. "Any more laughter and you're all fired," he grumbled as he made his way to the ladder.

It wasn't until he reached the ground that he realized how filthy he was. He self-consciously rubbed his hands against his pant legs as he walked toward her and took in her appearance.

Since he'd never seen Liana in anything but jeans, his throat went dry as he took in her simple navy shirtwaist dress that sported a pristine white collar. The dress was demure in design, but Sam realized that nothing Liana wore would ever look demure on her. Her lush curves and long slender legs that he'd heretofore only imagined incited a man's most erotic fantasies.

His libido automatically kicked into gear and he forced his gaze to her face. "Hi," he said when he reached her.

"Hi," she repeated. "I hope I'm not interrupting anything important, but I needed to talk to you."

Liana hoped her voice hadn't sounded as shrill to him as it had to her, but she was having a difficult time keeping her eyes off his bare chest which was much wider than she'd imagined, much more muscular, and definitely hairier.

She tried concentrating on his face, but found it as disconcerting as the rest of him when he rubbed his forearm against his forehead above his handkerchief sweatband. There was something innately sexy about a man who'd been indulging in hard physical labor.

"What's the problem?" he asked.

"I'm, uh, having some car trouble, and I wondered if you could pick me up at the garage tomorrow. I would have called you at home, but I don't have your home number. I suppose I could have left a message with your secretary, but when she told me you were nearby, I thought I'd check it out with you personally."

Liana knew she was babbling, but Sam had started rubbing his bare stomach, and she couldn't help but follow the action. She jerked her head up when she realized that her eyes were tracking the narrow line of hair that disappeared into his waistband, making her libido rear its head.

"What's wrong with your car?"

Liana blinked to assimilate his words. "It's missing."

He grinned. "As in lost or as in chugging down the road?"

"As in chugging down the road."

"It's probably the spark plugs. Want me to take a look?"

"I couldn't impose."

"You aren't imposing. Where are you parked?"

Liana pointed down the street.

Sam nodded and said, "Let me get my shirt and tell the guys I'm leaving. Then you can follow me to my place and I'll check it out. If it's the plugs, I can change them for you."

"Sam, you don't need to do that."

"What are friends for?" he said. Then, without giving her a chance to respond, he turned and walked away from her.

Yes, what are friends for? she repeated inwardly. The problem was, she knew that what was simmering between her and Sam was a far cry from friendship. She also knew she couldn't let those feelings flow.

She'd managed to come up with a refusal, but all her objections went out the window when he returned and said, "I'm glad you showed up. I've had one hell of a day, and I can't think of any better therapy than doctoring a sick car. I'm right over here. I'll wait for you, and then you can follow me home."

Liana nodded again, albeit reluctantly, and then headed for her car, telling herself that she really should commit herself for psychiatric evaluation. She felt like a schizophrenic whose rational side was being overwhelmed by her irrational one, and there wasn't a blessed thing she could do about it.

When she pulled up beside his car, he got out and walked around to her window.

"Let me drive your car so I can get an idea of what's wrong, and you can drive mine," he told her. "You can drive a stick shift, can't you?"

"It's been a long time since I've driven one," she said, paling. It had been a little more than three years, and she shook her head in an effort to erase the unsettling memories. But no matter how hard she tried, she couldn't dismiss them, and she found herself once again thrust back in time....

She kept trying to get the Jeep into gear, but the transmission wouldn't cooperate, and it's high-pitched whine was driving her crazy. Not that she wasn't already crazy. She'd been driving through rugged jungle terrain for hours and had no idea where she was. The back wheels of the Jeep had slid off the trail and into a deep rut. She knew she could get out if she could just get the transmission to engage, but it wasn't cooperating. It was so eerie here, so silent except for the hum of insects, which had become a din. God, she hated bugs and even though she couldn't see them, her skin began to cringe at the thought of them crawling all over her.

It was more than she could bear, and she leaped out of the Jeep and started running. She tore through heavy vegetation that whipped at her body and clutched at her hair, but she couldn't escape the insects. No matter how hard she ran, she couldn't escape the insects....

"Liana?" Sam said as he reached through her car window and touched her shoulder. He constantly found it amazing that the most mundane conversation could send her spinning off into oblivion. She was not only as white as a sheet, but she had a white-knuckled grip on the steering wheel. He wanted to peel her fingers away from it and kiss each and every one of them.

She started beneath his touch and blinked several times in rapid succession before she said, "I'd probably grind your gears, Sam. Why don't I just follow you and you can take my car out for a test drive when we get to your house?"

"Apartment," Sam corrected.

"Whatever."

He studied her through narrowed eyes, trying to decide if she was okay. But it appeared that whatever had happened was over, because her hand was resting loosely on the steering wheel and her color had returned.

When they arrived at his modest apartment building a short time later, Sam helped Liana out of her car. As he led her toward his apartment, he told her, "It isn't the Ritz, but it's home. It's also close to the office, which is something I really appreciate. I spent too many years commuting in rush hour traffic, which played havoc with my blood pressure."

Since his words didn't demand a response, Liana remained silent as he unlocked his door and stepped back for her to precede him. She let out a small gasp of surprise when she walked inside, for the first thing she saw was a collage of photographs on the wall that she immediately recognized. It was the limited edition series of photographs she'd taken of endangered species several years ago.

"As you can see, I was a fan of yours before we ever met," Sam said. "Would you like something to drink? I don't have any tea, but I do have a few cans of cola and ginger ale. I think I also have some beer left over from a poker game if you'd like something with a little more punch."

Before Liana could tell him that she'd like a glass of ice water, Sam said, "You probably prefer white wine, but I'm afraid I don't have any. Personally, I can't stand the stuff, which used to irritate the hell out of Kay. She said it showed a lack of breeding. I suppose she's right."

Liana automatically bristled at his ex-wife's accusation. As far as she was concerned a man's breeding couldn't be measured by what he drank, but by what he was on the inside, and Sam had enough heart to be royalty.

Even though Liana wasn't particularly fond of beer, she said, "I'd love a beer."

Sam smiled. "Great. How about a sandwich? I didn't stop for lunch today, and I'm starving."

"A sandwich would be nice."

Sam glanced down at himself and gave a wry shake of his head. "I know this won't sound very host-like, but I'm filthy and there's no sense in cleaning up until I've checked out your car. Would you mind making the sandwiches?"

"I wouldn't mind."

Sam left her in the kitchen and went to get his tools. When he returned, he settled on a stool at the breakfast bar and watched her work. Somehow, the domestic scene seemed right—too right—and he decided that he needed to indulge in some conversation.

"So what's the story on Adriane?"

"I don't know yet," Liana answered with a rueful smile. "She said she was too tired to talk last night, and when I tried to get her up this morning, she said no normal person got up before noon."

"Sounds like good, wholesome avoidance," Sam said with a chuckle. "And how'd it go at the bank?"

"Good, I think. You know how bankers are. They wear only one expression, so you can't really tell what they're thinking. But the fact that I've been running the business for the past three years should go in my favor."

"It should," Sam agreed, chagrined by the fact that he'd already run out of polite conversation. "Thanks," he said when Liana put his sandwich in front of him and handed him a beer.

"Do you believe this weather?" Liana asked, unknowingly sharing Sam's uneasiness over the domestic scene. "It must be seventy-five degrees out there."

"Yeah," Sam muttered as he watched her pop open a beer for herself and then round the bar. There was a stool between them, but he could still smell the delicate scent of her perfume. It wasn't as if he hadn't smelled it before, because his car was permeated with it. But for some crazy reason he was more cognizant of it today. "It's not unusual to have a bout of summer weather, but we both know it won't last. By this time next week, we'll probably have ten inches of snow."

"That's true," Liana murmured. "Colorado weather is fickle."

"Oh, hell," Sam said as he threw the remainder of his sandwich onto his plate. "Why are we talking about the weather?"

Liana slowly pivoted her head toward him. When she met his eyes, which were dark with frustration and something far more elemental, she quivered, because she knew that like her, Sam was recalling their kiss yesterday. "Because it's safe," she whispered.

"I don't want to be safe," he said as he reached out and caught a handful of her hair. It seemed to take forever for it to sift through his fingers, and when the tips finally grazed his palm, he closed his hand over them, unwilling to let them go.

"You know, I almost punched a man in the nose today because of his chauvinistic attitude, but right now I'm having a few chauvinistic thoughts myself."

"Oh?" Liana said, telling herself that she should be high-tailing it out of here, but unable to convince her body to move. "Just what are you thinking?"

"That it should be against the law for a woman to cut her hair." He released his hold on her hair and watched it fall across her breast and down to her waist. "So, how is Hool-ligan?"

"That was a swift change of subject," she noted, knowing that she was playing with fire, but mesmerized by the flames just the same.

Sam shrugged, propped his foot on the rung of the stool between them and rested his arm on his knee. "I decided to spare you from the rest of my chauvinistic notions because you'd probably slap my face."

"That bad, huh?"

"Yeah," Sam said with a short laugh. "I'd better go check on your car. Where are your keys?"

Liana fished them out of the pocket of her full skirt. Sam took them, grabbed his tool box and left with a, "Feel free to make yourself at home."

Liana wasn't hungry any longer, but she forced herself to finish her sandwich, washing it down with sips of beer. Then she wrapped the remainder of Sam's sandwich in plastic wrap, washed up the utensils she'd used and put them away.

Even though Sam had given her permission to make herself at home, she felt uncomfortable as she roamed around his living room. It was a typical bachelor pad with heavy overstuffed furniture, a television set, an elaborate stereo system, and newspapers and magazines scattered around the room.

She found herself automatically tidying up by straightening the magazines, putting the newspapers into a pile, and taking the few dirty dishes he'd left in the room into the kitchen. When she got ready to wash them, however, she realized that Sam might take offense at her actions, so she left the dishes in the sink.

She'd just settled on the sofa when Sam opened the door and said, "Liana, there's a small red box of socket wrenches on the floor of my bedroom closet. I'm covered with grease, so would you get them and bring them out to me?"

"Of course. Where's your bedroom?"

"Down the hall. Second door on the left."

She walked down the hallway, but was reluctant to enter his bedroom when she stood in the open doorway. His king-size bed was an unmade jumble of blankets and sheets. He'd tossed his clothes over a chair until he had a small mountain of laundry, and he had scattered half a dozen pairs of socks around the floor. It was apparent that Sam hadn't mastered the art of neatness, and Liana felt an affinity with him. This could have been her own room a few years ago.

She reminded herself that Sam was waiting, and she forced herself to walk to his closet. She smiled when she opened the door and found it a disorganized horror. His wardrobe was crammed into one corner, and the remainder of the closet was filled with everything from a basketball to some kind of tool that she didn't even recognize. Sam might appreciate his apartment, but Liana reached the conclusion that the man definitely needed a house with a double-car garage.

It took her a moment to find the red box of socket wrenches, which was sandwiched between a three-foot high stack of fishing magazines and, of all things, a two-drawer file cabinet. She held her breath as she pulled it out, certain the stack of magazines would collapse. But all it did was sway slightly before it settled back into place, and she quickly closed the door before disaster could befall her.

A minute later she joined Sam at her car. He was bent under the hood, his shirt once again gone, and he glanced up and gave her an absent smile.

"Good, you found it. Just put it by the tool box."

"What do you think is wrong?" Liana asked as she complied with his request.

"Fouled plugs. I'll clean them and then you should be as good as new."

"You really don't have to do this, Sam. I know that car work can be a pain in the neck, and I can take it to the garage tomorrow."

Sam stood up and leaned his hip against the grille of her car, fighting against the anger stirring inside him. Kay had hated the fact that he liked to tinker with cars, and they'd had more arguments than he cared to remember over his "filthy" hobby. He kept telling himself that Liana wasn't trying to denigrate him, but maybe she didn't trust him to work on her car. He didn't like to think that was the case, but he did understand her reasoning if it was. After all, she had no way of knowing if he really knew a gas cap from a spark plug.

"Are you trying to tell me you'd prefer to have a certified mechanic do the work?"

He was smiling as he asked the question, but Liana could sense an underlying tension. It wasn't exactly hostility, but she had a feeling that it was close to it. If she didn't know better, she'd think that she'd somehow offended him.

"No. What I'm trying to tell you is that you don't have to feel obligated to fix my car. I'm sure you have better things to do."

The tension immediately faded, and he reached out and smeared a spot of grease on the end of her nose. "Better things, maybe, but nothing that would be as much fun. Want to keep me company?"

"Sure."

"Great. There are a couple of lawn chairs in the back of my car. If you want to dig the keys out of my right pocket, you can get one and sit back and relax while I work."

Liana was certain he had to be kidding. He couldn't really expect her to put her hand in his pocket. But he angled his right hip toward her and Liana gulped as her gaze landed on the worn denims that hung so low on his hips she was sure a sneeze would make them fall off.

"It's okay," he said, laughter vibrating in his voice. "All you'll find down there are some keys, a pocket knife and maybe a little change. I promise, there are no surprises."

Liana glanced up, ready to tell him that she didn't need the chair, but his eyes were gleaming with challenge, daring her to make a dive for his keys. Never one to resist a dare, she took a deep breath and stuck her hand down his pocket, discovering that his pants were such a tight fit that all she could do was hook her fingers around his keys and drag them out. She accomplished the task in a matter of a few seconds, but it had felt as if it had taken forever. She also knew she was flushed, and it didn't have a blessed thing to do with the heat.

"It's the key with the black rubber on the end," Sam said as he stuck his head back under the hood of her car, knowing that he was about to burst into laughter, and he didn't think Liana would appreciate his mirth.

He peeked out when she walked toward the back of his car, and he shook his head as he watched her hair sway around her body in a shimmering veil. He wondered what she'd say if he told her the kinds of fantasies his mind was conjuring up concerning her long, silken tresses. Hell, forget the tresses, he decided when she leaned into the back to haul out the chair and a breeze caught her skirt, lifting it high enough to give him an ample view of her thigh. Thankfully, she'd already retrieved his keys, because right now he'd be able to promise her a good surprise.

With a soft curse, Sam returned his attention to the spark plugs. He wasn't supposed to be ogling the woman, he was supposed to be working on her engine. Boy, would he like to work on her engine—and he wasn't talking about the one that had come from Detroit!

"So, how long have you been working on cars?" Liana asked when she opened the lawn chair and sat down.

"Since the day I turned seventeen and bought my first car," he answered. "Money was always short around our house, and even though I was working, I was giving most of my salary to my mother. I couldn't afford the luxury of dropping my car off at a garage, particularly since it was so old that everything on it was about worn out. I think I just about rebuilt it from the ground up. It was my pride and joy, and it nearly killed me to sell it.''

"So, why did you?"

He pulled out a spark plug and reached for a rag. As he began to clean it, he said, "Because Kay wanted a new car, and we couldn't afford the insurance on both. We'd only been married a few months, and I didn't have the heart to deny her anything, particularly when she claimed that she didn't feel the car was reliable and was always afraid it would break down and leave her stranded somewhere. I was too young and foolish to realize I was being manipulated.''

"How old were you when you got married?"

"Nineteen."

"Nineteen?" Liana repeated in disbelief. "Good heavens, you were a child groom, weren't you?"

He cocked his head to the side as though considering her words. "Young, yes. A child? No. I think reformed rebel would be a better description. When I was sixteen, I was hell on wheels. I was expelled from school for fighting. I was arrested and put on probation for shoplifting. My grandfather said I was heading down the path of destruction, and I was eagerly looking forward to reaching the end of that path."

"So, what happened to turn you around?" Liana asked, totally absorbed in his story. She couldn't even envision the man standing before her as the rebellious teenager he was describing.

"My grandfather took me into the mountains."

"That's the trip you told me about," Liana murmured.

"Yeah," Sam confirmed. "I didn't want to go, because I didn't want to spend two weeks listening to him spout his philosophies and quotes from the Bible. But he ignored my protests and hauled me up there kicking and screaming.''

He paused, and a smile of remembrance curved his lips. "For the first two days, we didn't speak a word. We went on horseback, and I sullenly rode behind him, ignoring my surroundings. But eventually the scenery wore me down. There were meadows of wild flowers so vibrant with color they hurt my eyes. There were bubbling creeks swollen with the run off of melting snow, and the water was so clear I could watch trout swim by. Early one morning, I stood on top of a cliff and watched a deer give birth to a fawn, and I was awed by the experience. Before I even knew what was happening, the cold lump of anger inside me began to melt."

"And why were you so angry?" Liana questioned softly.

Sam frowned as he removed another spark plug, and he tossed it from one hand to the other, not certain if he wanted to answer the question. He'd never talked with anyone about his father's suicide, not even his ex-wife. But then, he'd never talked with anyone but Liana about Kay's desertion, either. It hurt to admit that two people he'd loved deeply had been able to abandon him without a second thought. It also made him insecure enough to believe that there might be something wrong with him.

He shook his head to dismiss those painful, introspective thoughts. Life went on, and he'd long ago set those emotional seasons of winter behind him. But if that declaration was true, shouldn't he be feeling acceptance instead of pain?

"I was angry because my father walked out to the garage one day, turned on the car and gassed himself. The coroner ruled it a suicide."

"I'm very sorry, Sam," Liana said, her voice filled with compassion. "Losing your father like that must have been awful."

"Yeah," he responded gruffly, beginning to clean the spark plug as the events of that long-ago day surfaced. "The worst part was that he didn't even have the courtesy to leave us a note and tell us why he'd done it. I don't think I'll ever be able to forgive him for that."

Liana's heart went out to him as she watched his lips thin into a grim line and a muscle twitch wildly along his strong jawline. She could feel the pain radiating from him, and cursed the fact that she had once again inadvertently touched on a tender subject. She did, however, now understand his reaction yesterday when they'd been discussing his mother's engagement and he'd said his father had given up his rights to that picture a long time ago.

She was out of the chair and in front of him before she even knew what she was doing, and when she reached out to put her arms around him, he said, "Hey, I'm okay, and I don't want you to get that pretty dress all dirty."

"To hell with the dress," she said as she gave him a hug.

Sam told himself that this was crazy as he automatically linked his arms around her and hugged her back. She was so warm, and she felt so right against him. He nuzzled his nose against her hair, inhaling the clean scent of her shampoo, and the oddest thing began to happen.

He knew he'd never be able to come completely to grips with his father's death because of the nagging guilt that hovered over him, but suddenly he felt as if he might be able to find a measure of peace.

"You're an angel," he said as he caught her chin and raised her face. "A veritable angel."

Her eyes darkened and she shook her head. "No, Sam. There is nothing angelic about me. If you only knew..."

"Knew what?" he asked when her voice trailed off.

"Nothing," Liana said, raising on tiptoe and pressing her lips to his to stop his questions.

She liked Sam. She liked him more than she wanted to admit, and she couldn't bear the thought of how he'd react if he ever learned the truth about her.

When she finally pulled away, Sam released a long breath and said, "If you keep that up, I'll never get your motor started."

Liana laughed softly as she reached up and ran her hand along his jaw, enjoying the raspy feel of his five o'clock shadow, even if it was only three in the afternoon. "I think you've already accomplished that."

He arched a brow and gave her a wicked smile. "Well, in that case, how would you feel about going up to my apartment and taking a look at my etchings?"

Liana knew he was only joking, or was he? She saw desire burning in his eyes, and she reacted to it with a deep pang of longing. But the even stronger pull was an emotional one, because she could sense that Sam was still hurting over the memory of his father's death. She'd opened the wound, so wasn't she responsible for closing it again?

Every decent cell in her body said she couldn't make love with Sam, but her heart kept arguing otherwise. Would it be so wrong to offer herself to him as a balm for his pain? Probably, but she wasn't interested in probabilities right now. She was interested in Sam, and she couldn't stand to see him upset.

"I think those are my etchings hanging on your wall. However, maybe we should look at them to make sure."

Sam blinked, sure he was misunderstanding her. He'd only been teasing her. Well, half-teasing, because ever since he'd laid eyes on her, he'd wanted her. But if he made love with her, he knew he'd be taking a chance of losing his heart to her, and he really didn't know a thing about her. Was he willing to take the risk?

Yes, he decided as he gazed down into her beautiful face. Oh, Lord, yes.

"Are you sure this is what you want?" he asked.

Liana answered by kissing him again.

SAM WAS CERTAIN HE'D DIED and gone to heaven as he sat on the toilet in his bathroom and watched Liana disrobe. He'd offered his assistance, but she'd demurred, and now he was glad that she had.

He'd always known she was beautiful, but he'd never realized just how beautiful. Her body was fit and trim and the only flaw he could see was a small mole on her inner left thigh that was revealed when she peeled off her panty hose.

When she was standing before him in nothing but her bra and panties, she leaned forward and caught her extraordinarily long hair in her hand, securing it with the rubber band she'd dug out of her purse. Then she wrapped it into a loose knot on top of her head and secured it with the bobby pins that she'd also taken from her purse.

"Your turn," she said as she leaned back against the door and smiled at him.

Sam had already shed his shoes and socks, and he dropped his pants in an instant.

"I'm sorry I got you all dirty," he said, but there wasn't one ounce of contrition in his voice.

She pushed the straps of her bra off her shoulders and began to snap open the front closure. "Water conservation is a very good cause."

"Yeah," Sam stated roughly when she dropped her bra to the floor. Her full breasts were high and crowned with rose-tipped nipples. He closed his eyes and told himself that good things came to those who waited. It was the only way he could maintain control.

She turned on the shower and then faced him as she hooked a finger beneath the elastic at her waist. "So, what do you say? Shall we both do it on the count of three?"

"Who has time to count?" Sam replied as he stripped off his jockey shorts and strode toward her.

He pulled her into his arms and kissed her hard while slipping his hands beneath her panties and pushing them off her hips. She did a complicated shimmy that was as arousing as effective, and the satin slid to her feet. Sam wanted to drop her to the floor and take her right there.

But when he looked into her eyes the urgency died. He wanted her so badly that he felt as if he were ready to explode into a million pieces, but he needed to savor her more.

"Sam?" Liana whispered uncertainly as she watched the expression on his face change from raw desire to tenderness.

"It's okay," he murmured as he pressed a kiss to her forehead. "We have all the time in the world, so let's take advantage of it."

"But—"

"Shh," he said. "Just let me love you."

He pulled her into the shower, where he washed her body so tenderly that Liana felt as if she were the most cherished object in the world. He was so sweet and so gentle with her that her heart ached and her eyes were flooded with tears when he pulled her back out of the shower and dried her before he took care of himself.

Then he swung her up into his arms and carried her to his bed. When he lowered over her, prepared to enter her, he caught her head in his hands and tangled his fingers in her hair.

"It's time for a change of seasons, Liana," he said. "Share the beauty of spring with me."

Liana knew that what he was asking was an impossible dream. By the very nature of her sins, she could never undergo a change of seasons. But she did care enough for this man to make a short foray into spring. Over the next few weeks she'd give him all she had to give. She only prayed that she wouldn't commit the ultimate sin of falling in love.

Chapter Nine

The day was so bright and clear that Liana could see for miles. A little boy danced up to her and handed her a flower. She didn't know the flower's name, but it was bright red and beautiful.

She laughed as she accepted the flower and broke off a piece of the panfried dough that sat in front of her, popping it into her mouth. The batter was so light that she didn't have to chew. It truly melted in her mouth.

"More flowers?" the boy asked as he continued to dance around her, his face reflecting the carnival atmosphere of the crowd milling through the street.

"How much?" Liana asked.

"Nada," the boy answered.

"Nothing?"

"Not for the pretty lady," he said. "What color?"

"Red."

He dashed to the nearby flower cart, extracted every red flower and brought them to her. He bowed deeply when she accepted them, but Liana recoiled in horror when he raised upright, his mouth open in a silent scream as the blood pumped through his chest.

His scream may have been silent, but hers was real as she bolted up in bed.

"Liana!" Sam cried in distress as he sat up beside her. He instantly wrapped his arms around her and held her close. "It's all right," he murmured. "It's all right. It was just a nightmare."

"No," Liana whispered on a sob as she clung to him desperately. "It wasn't a dream. It was real."

When she trembled violently against him, Sam pulled her back down to the mattress and tucked the covers around them. Her body was hot, almost feverish, but her teeth were chattering, and he could feel the terror radiating from her. He wrapped himself around her and cradled her protectively, wondering what kind of nightmare could have such a terrible effect on her. He'd never seen anything like this.

"It's going to be all right," he whispered against her hair. "It's going to be all right, Liana. I promise, it's going to be all right."

But Liana knew that his words were nothing more than an attempt at pacification. No one could ever take the horror away, not even Sam.

THE MOMENT LIANA regained control, her terror was replaced with panic, because she knew Sam would question her about the dream. She felt so vulnerable lying here naked in his arms, and she feared he might get more information out of her than she could afford to reveal. What she needed was the armor of her clothes. It was the only way she could deal with him. She had to get to her clothes.

When she tried to pull away from him, however, he tightened his hold around her. She levered her head so she could see his face, and the moment her gaze collided with his, her panic increased twofold. His eyes were not only filled with concern, they were also filled with determination.

"Please, let me get up, Sam," she whispered hoarsely.

"In a minute," he said as he brushed her hair away from her face. "Tell me about your dream. When something frightens you that badly, you need to talk it out."

She shook her head. "Please, Sam, just let me get up. I think I'm going to be sick." And it wasn't a lie. Her stomach was positively roiling with fear.

Sam frowned down at her, torn over granting her request, because he had the distinct impression that she was trying to hide something from him, but what? She'd had a nightmare, for heaven's sake, so it didn't make any sense.

But he suddenly recalled that she'd told him the dream was real. Was that why she was acting like this? Had the dream been about whatever she claimed she couldn't discuss because of national security?

He wanted to ask, but he didn't, because she was growing paler by the minute. He decided to let her up and ask his questions later.

The moment Sam released his hold on her, Liana leaped out of bed and dashed into the bathroom, slamming and locking the door behind her. She leaned back against it and crossed her arms over her stomach, telling herself to relax. She had to get herself under control, because she knew that when she faced Sam again, she had to be calm.

Why had she let herself fall asleep? Why? She should have never let herself fall asleep.

When the door rattled unexpectedly, she jumped away from it, barely holding back a startled scream.

"Liana, are you all right?" Sam questioned in concern.

"I'm fine, Sam. Just fine. I'm getting dressed and I'll be out in a minute."

"You're sure you're okay?"

"Yes. I'm fine."

"All right," he said, and Liana sighed in relief when she heard him release the doorknob.

While she dressed, she forced herself to take deep, calming breaths. By the time she was done she felt much better, but she still had to consciously will her hands to keep from twisting together when she walked out of the bathroom.

Sam had also dressed, and he was lying across the foot of his bed, his head propped up on his hand. He was watching her through hooded eyes, so she couldn't read his mood, and her panic started to return.

"Feeling better?" he asked, his voice as neutral as white on white.

Liana nodded.

"Good, because I think it's time we had a talk, don't you?" he said.

"I think it's time that I got home," Liana replied, unconsciously raising her chin a defiant notch. "I know I called Adriane, but it's getting late and I don't want her to worry about me."

"Then call her again and tell her you'll be home shortly. We need to talk."

Liana shook her head. "Talking would only be a waste of time, Sam, because I can't tell you what you want to know. That nightmare was about my past, and I've already explained that it's a matter of national security."

Sam came up off the bed so fast that Liana automatically took a step back. She wasn't afraid of him, but she was intimidated, especially when he walked toward her in an easy, loose-limbed gait that was almost predatory.

When he stopped in front of her, Liana gazed up at him warily. She frowned when he popped open the top two buttons of her dress. Was he going to try to seduce her to get his answers? Just the thought that he might consider resorting to such a base level made her angry, and she welcomed the ire, because it stiffened her resolve.

But Sam made it quite clear that seduction wasn't on his mind when he said. "Now you won't choke to death on your half-truths."

Liana bristled. "Are you calling me a liar?"

"No. But I'm not going to let you crawl into that smoke screen of national security, either. Maybe you can't give me the details of what happened to you, but you can tell me what's going on inside you. Your feelings can't be a matter of national security."

"You don't know what you're talking about," Liana snapped as she spun away from him and marched toward the door, knowing that she was telling him an outright lie. Not only could she discuss her feelings, but there were a lot of the details she could tell him without violating national security. It had been those details that she'd shared with her parents, and the memory of their reaction made her shudder. If her parents had reacted that horribly, she could imagine how Sam would react. There was no way she'd expose herself to that.

"The hell I don't know what I'm talking about." He caught her arm and spun her back around to face him.

"Let me go, Sam," she ordered softly, warningly.

"No." He gripped her shoulders and gave her a frustrated shake. "Dammit, Liana, I just held you in my arms and felt you coming apart at the seams. You're terrified, and if you don't come to grips with your feelings, you're going to lose your mind."

"Well, it's my mind, and I'll lose it if I want to."

His lips lifted in a sardonic smile. "But I'm not going to stand by and let that happen to you. You're far too beautiful and far too talented to spend the rest of your life vegetating in the middle of a nightmare, and I'm going to drag you out of it if I have to do it with you kicking and screaming all the way."

"Is that a variation of the old saying, I'm giving you fair warning?" she drawled sarcastically.

"You hit the nail right on the head."

"Well, you can forget it, Sam." She jerked away from him. "Just because I made love with you doesn't give you the right to interfere in my life, but since you seem to think it does, I can guarantee that we won't be making love again."

"Oh, yes, we will." He pulled her against him and tangled his fingers in her hair, staring down at her with determination. "You can run from yourself, but you aren't going to run from me. What happened in that bed was wonderful for both of us, and I'm not going to turn my back on it because you want to play ostrich and stick your head in the sand. Now, let's get you home. As you said, we don't want Adriane to worry."

They were silent all the way to her house, and Liana wanted to stomp her foot in frustration when Sam walked her to her door and dropped a quick peck on her cheek. Then he turned and walked back to his car, whistling a cheerful tune. He was *whistling,* for heaven's sake!

Liana gulped, because she suddenly realized that Sam the mountain mover was back, and what Sam wanted Sam got. But as panic set in again, Liana got mad. Mad at Sam for presuming that because she'd made love with him he had the right to interfere in her life, and mad at herself because she'd known from the beginning that he was not a man to form a casual alliance. By succumbing to her desire, she'd played right into his hands. How in the world was she going to get herself out of this mess?

She'd have to keep her distance from him. She'd have to make sure that their relationship went back to that of employer-employee. If she didn't, he might discover the truth, and she could never allow that.

"HOW DARE YOU BRING a television into my house without my permission," Liana railed as she snapped off the blazing television set and glared at her sister. "You're supposed to be thinking, not watching television!"

"Geez, who rang your bell?" Adriane muttered. "And I can think and watch television at the same time. I don't have a one-track mind, you know. Besides, it's boring in this tomb. How do you stand it?"

"It's very easy. It's called peace and quiet. Did you feed Hooligan as I asked you to?"

"Oops." The young woman scrambled off the sofa and ran toward the kitchen.

Liana forced herself to count to ten. She wasn't going to lose her temper, because she knew that she wouldn't just be reacting to Adriane's irresponsibility. She'd also be taking out on the girl her anger with Sam.

"Why in the world didn't you get a decent cat?" Adriane asked in disgust when she strolled back into the room. "That one is so ugly that he gives me the creeps."

"Beauty is only skin deep, and it's time you learned that," Liana replied irritably. "Now, sit down. We're going to have that talk that you were too tired to have last night."

"I came here to think, not to get a lecture," Adriane grumbled as she plopped back down on the sofa and gave Liana an irritated look. "If I wanted lectures, I would have stayed at home."

"I'm not going to lecture you. I want to know exactly what is going on between you and Mom and Dad."

"I told you last night. They won't let me grow up."

"What is it that you want to do that they don't think you're grown up enough to do?"

"How in the world did you say all of that in one breath?"

Liana balled up her fist and tapped it against her thigh as she sat down in the chair. "Adriane, I've had a long and frustrating day, and I don't have the patience to sit here and pull teeth to get a straight answer out of you. What is going on?''

The girl bounced up off the sofa and began to pace around the room. "All of this is your fault, you know."

"My fault?" Liana repeated incredulously. "How could it be my fault? I haven't even been around for the past three years."

"Exactly." Adriane came to a stop, propped her hands on her hips and scowled at Liana. "When you took off, Mom cried for weeks. *Weeks,* Liana. And it wasn't just the sniffles. She bawled her head off. I don't know what you said to her, but whatever it was it tore her to pieces."

Liana immediately became defensive at the accusatory tone in her sister's voice. "I'm sorry Mom was so upset, but there were things going on that you can't possibly understand and I can't explain. Please, believe me when I say that I never meant to make Mom so upset, but Dad was there to help her."

"Oh, sure. Let's talk about Dad," Adriane muttered as she slashed her hand through the air. "He's the strong, silent type, right? When he gets upset, he just gets stronger and more silent. After you left, he got so strong and so silent that it was like living with a zombie!"

"I'm sorry," Liana whispered miserably. She'd known her parents had been upset, but she hadn't known that they'd reacted so drastically over her story. Now that she did, she was flooded with guilt. Why had she told them what had happened? Why hadn't she just kept her mouth shut?

Because she'd hated herself and she'd wanted them to hate her too, she suddenly realized, frowning for she also realized that she'd been telling herself that she was ignoring them to protect them. Now, she wondered if she hadn't stayed away to punish them for loving her despite what she'd done.

She wanted to think the matter through, but Adriane interrupted her thoughts by saying, "You're sorry? You don't even know what sorry is, because when Mom and Dad started to pull themselves together, I became their security blanket. I couldn't even breathe without one of them checking on me."

"They've always been overprotective of you, and you know it," Liana defended.

"Sure, but it became an obsession. I was being overdosed on love." The girl raked her hand through her shoulder-length hair. "I will admit that at first I didn't complain, because I'm spoiled rotten. I even took advantage of the situation. They were so devoted to me that all I had to do was ask for something and it was there. But after I started college, I wanted some freedom. Mom and Dad wouldn't even let me move into the dorm, because they were afraid something bad would happen to me and they wouldn't be there to bail me out when it did."

"Again, that's understandable," Liana said. "You haven't shown much responsibility over the years."

"And how am I supposed to become responsible if I'm never allowed to make my own mistakes?"

"You have a point there," Liana conceded.

"You're darn right, I have a point. I can't grow up without some freedom."

"So that's what this is all about. You're simply fighting a battle for your independence."

"Well, sort of," Adriane hedged.

Liana arched a brow. "What do you mean, sort of? It is or it isn't."

"Well, it is, but..."

"But?"

"I want to join the Marine Corps."

Liana was so flabbergasted by the announcement that she could have been knocked over by a feather. "Why in the world do you want to join the Marine Corps?"

"Because it's tough," Adriane answered. "If I can make it through boot camp, I can make it through anything. Don't you see," she said as she dropped down to her knees in front of Liana and caught her hands. "I need to find out how strong I am, because if I don't, I'm just going to keep tripping through life as a bubble head. Do you want a sister who's a bubble head?"

Liana reached out and smoothed the girl's hair. "I'd love you, bubble head or not."

"I know that, but it isn't your love that's important here. It's my self-esteem. In the Marine Corps I won't be rich little Adriane Stevens. I'll be just another uniform who is expected to do her job like everyone else. And I know I can do it, Liana. I just need the chance to prove it. I'm old enough to join without Mom and Dad's permission, but I don't want to do that to them. I want to leave with their blessing, so will you help me convince them that I'm doing the right thing? I know they'd listen to you. They've always listened to you."

Liana closed her eyes to shut out the pleading look on Adriane's face. What she was asking was impossible. After the way Liana had screwed up her own life, her parents would never listen to her, and even if they would, could she really face them? And she knew that that's what it would come down to, because they'd never agree to Adriane's wild idea without a face-to-face confrontation.

She opened her eyes, determined to give Adriane an unequivocal no, but as she stared down at her, she couldn't bring herself to do it. It was several moments before she realized that it was because Adriane had exhibited a good deal of maturity when she'd said that she could join without their parents' permission, but she didn't want to do that to them. It was also because Liana feared the girl might be right when she claimed that their overprotective attitude was Liana's fault. She'd been lecturing Adrian on maturity, but she hadn't shown much of it herself when she'd run away rather than staying and facing her problems. By separating herself from her parents, she'd forced them into picking up the pieces by turning their full attention on the one chick left in the nest.

"I'll make you a deal," she finally said. "If you can prove to me during the next few weeks that you are a responsible adult, I'll stand behind you one hundred percent."

"Oh, thank you!" Adriane exclaimed with a laugh as she threw her arms around Liana. "I promise you that you won't be sorry."

"I'm sure I won't," Liana murmured.

"Now, what about the television set? Can I keep it?"

Liana frowned "How did you get it, anyway? I had the car."

"I called a rental company and had it delivered. So, can I keep it?"

"Only if you take it into your room," Liana answered. "I need my peace and quiet."

"Great!"

Liana shook her head as she watched Adriane haul the portable set down the hallway to the guest room with Hooligan trailing behind her. With all the changes taking place in her life, she might as well give up and go ahead and subscribe to the newspaper and hang pictures on the wall. It was probably already a fait accompli that she would end up doing so.

WHEN HER PHONE RANG, Liana groped for the instrument and brought it to her ear with a sleepily mumbled, "Hello?"

"Oh, damn, I woke you," Sam stated gruffly. "Sorry, but I thought you'd be up. It's snowing."

"Just a minute," Liana said, still too groggy to assimilate what Sam was saying. She laid the receiver on the nightstand and forced herself to sit up. Then she hit the light on her alarm clock. The alarm would have gone off in another fifteen minutes, but she'd had so many nightmares during the night that she felt as if she hadn't slept a wink.

The wind rattled her bedroom window, and the rest of Sam's words hit her. Hooligan grumbled vociferously when she tossed back the covers and leaped out of bed, jolting him from his cocoon beneath the blankets.

"It *is* snowing!" she exclaimed in disbelief as she gazed out the window. When she'd told Sam yesterday that Colorado weather was fickle, she hadn't expected it to turn around and prove how fickle it was. And it wasn't just snowing, it looked like a full-blown blizzard.

"Liana?" she heard Sam yell through the phone.

She rushed back to the nightstand and grabbed the receiver. "Sorry. I needed a minute to wake up. You're right. It is snowing. What are we going to do?"

"Stay home," he said, with a chuckle. "The police have announced that only emergency vehicles are to be on the roads until further notice. If it's that bad down here, you know what it's like in the mountains."

"It'll be several days before we can get back into them."

"Right. I don't think we should even consider another trip until the middle of next week. How's Adriane?"

"Believe it or not, she's run away from home because she wants to join the Marine Corps."

Sam couldn't help bursting into laughter. "Sorry, but I just had a flash of a drill sergeant's face when he first meets

Adriane. If I were you, I'd get an option on the movie rights."

"I think it's already been done," Liana said with a sigh. "But she really is serious about this, and the more I think about it, the more convinced I am that it would be good for her. I guess I'll just have to wait and see what happens."

"Yes, I suppose you will. As soon as the snow lets up, I'll get your car running, and when the roads open, I'll bring it to you. Will you be all right until then?"

"Sure. If the roads are closed, we won't be going anywhere. In fact, Adriane says she wants me to teach her how to cook so she won't make a complete fool of herself when she's assigned to K.P. duty. That should make for an interesting day. I've always had a yearning for food poisoning."

Sam laughed again. "Well, you might as well crawl back into bed and go back to sleep until cooking lesson time."

"Yeah. You, too."

"Yeah." There was a long silence before he finally said, "How are you today?"

Liana suddenly realized that by trading casual conversation with him, she'd already broken the rule of going back to a business relationship. She gave a frustrated shake of her head and wondered if she was fighting a losing battle.

"I'm fine, Sam," she stated briskly. "I'll see you when you bring my car. Have a good day."

"You, too. Bye."

The phone went dead and Liana shivered as she replaced the receiver in its cradle, but she knew the shiver had little to do with the chilly room. It had to do with the wistful tone of Sam's voice that echoed the one in her heart, and her mind filled with images of him as they'd made love yesterday.

She knew she should be regretting that act because of Sam's behavior afterwards, but how could she possibly re-

gret something that had been so wonderful? For one infin-
itesimal moment, she considered forgetting a business
relationship and letting herself enjoy the little bit of time
she'd have with Sam.

But she knew she couldn't do that. Heaven help her, she
wanted to, but she couldn't, because Sam was already getting too close, and suddenly she feared that her heart might
be in more danger than her secrets.

SAM FELT RESTLESS after he hung up from Liana, and he
prowled through his apartment with the energy of a caged
animal.

Once again, his night had been plagued with dreams of
her, but this time he'd kept jumping up in bed to the sound
of Liana's chilling scream. What in the world had happened to her? And why was she refusing to face it?

He'd no more than formulated the questions when his
gaze landed on the box he'd brought home from his
mother's and stuffed into the corner. It was filled with his
father's things, and he hadn't wanted them. If he hadn't
feared that he'd hurt his mother's feelings, he would have
told her to throw them away, and it suddenly dawned on him
that he was refusing to do what he wanted Liana to do.
Confront his feelings and deal with them.

He carried the box to the kitchen table and forced himself to live through the memories as he took out each item.
There was his father's old fishing hat, with all his favorite
fishing flies still hooked to it, and Sam could vividly recall
the first time his father had taken him fishing. There was his
father's favorite book—a first edition copy of *The Maltese
Falcon*—which he'd read to Sam from cover to cover when
Sam had been in bed for a solid week with the flu. There was
the pocketknife that Sam had bought him one Christmas,
and the memories went on and on.

But it was the photographs that were the most poignant: his father dressed as a clown at his sixth birthday party; his father lifting him up into the air when he'd hit the home run and captured a trophy for his Little League baseball team; and, of course, that final photograph where he was holding up his first driver's license with his father standing beside him, grinning proudly.

That picture was the most difficult to handle, because it was an argument over his driving privileges that had driven a wedge between them two weeks later. Sam was still convinced that that argument had caused his father's death.

Tears welled in his eyes, but he blinked them back. He hadn't cried for his father twenty years ago, and he sure wasn't going to cry for him now. He also knew that it was finally time for him to get the guilt off his chest. He had to tell his mother what had happened.

SAM HAD FREQUENTLY WALKED the two miles to his mother's house, but he'd never done it before in a virtual blizzard. By the time he arrived he not only resembled a snowman, but felt as frozen as one.

"Good heavens, Sam, what's wrong?" Abigail asked in alarm when he arrived at her back door.

"Nothing," he answered as he shook off as much snow as he could before stepping inside. "I came to shovel your walks."

"At seven in the morning in the middle of a blizzard?" she inquired with skepticism.

Sam flashed her his best boyish smile as he shucked his outerwear and hung it on the coatrack inside the door. While he pulled off his boots, he said, "I also thought I'd talk you into fixing me breakfast."

"You risked pneumonia for one of my boring breakfasts? Now I know something's wrong," she muttered as she retrieved a mop from a nearby closet and handed it to him. "Clean up your mess."

Sam chuckled. "You're a good cook and you know it."

"I'm an unimaginative cook and you know it. Mop."

Sam obediently cleaned up the snow he'd tracked in. "Is Gramps up yet?"

Abigail glanced up from the refrigerator where she was retrieving bacon and eggs. "No. He won't be up for another couple of hours. Do you need to talk to him?"

"No, I need to talk to you," Sam replied as he opened the back door, squeezed out the mop and put it back in the closet.

When he turned to face his mother, he saw her worried frown and wished he could reassure her, but he couldn't. He had to talk to her about his father, and he wasn't sure how to broach the subject.

Abigail, as if realizing the profundity of his words, replaced the food in the refrigerator and then filled two mugs with coffee. After she settled at the table with him, she said, "So, tell me what's on your mind."

Sam gave an uncomfortable shrug and toyed with his coffee cup. "I want to talk about Dad."

"What about him?"

His voice was hoarse when he said, "Do you remember that terrible fight he and I had about my driving privileges the night before he . . . died."

"Yes, I do remember the fight. What about it?"

Sam gave a miserable shake of his head as he confessed, "I told him I hated him. I told him that I wished he was dead and that I'd be better off without him. I guess he took my words to heart."

"Oh, Sam, no," Abigail objected as she rose from her seat and came to his side. When she wrapped her arms around him, he felt like a child again and hated himself for it. That didn't stop him from circling his arms around her waist and holding on tight. "Your fight didn't have anything to do with your father's death," she assured him as she stroked his head.

Sam allowed himself to indulge in her motherly ministrations for a moment before reminding himself that he was a man and, as such, he had to take responsibility for his actions, even actions he'd performed as a rebellious teenager.

He eased away from her and said, "There's more to the story, and I've never been able to find the courage to tell you about it, but I have to. I have to get it off my chest."

Abigail sat back down and covered his hand with hers, giving it a reassuring squeeze. "Then, tell me about it."

"The next morning he tried to make peace with me, and I wouldn't let him," he confessed with a miserable sigh. "He started talking about all the things we were going to do at the father-and-son picnic at school, and I got up and walked away from him. I can still see the hurt look in his eyes when I did that. Every time, I think of him, that's the first image I get."

He was silent for several seconds before he continued. "The worst thing is, I almost relented. I almost told him I was sorry, but I was still so angry with him that I decided he deserved to suffer a little longer. Maybe if I had taken that one small step, given him something to look forward to, he'd still be alive."

"My word, Sam, don't be ridiculous!" Abigail exclaimed as she leaned forward, caught his face in her hands and forced him to look at her. "You were a sixteen-year-old boy. Your father was a thirty-six-year-old man. You can't make yourself responsible for his actions, and I don't believe he killed himself because you walked away from him. In fact, the more I think about it, the more convinced I am that he didn't even plan on doing it. I think he just walked out to the garage and something snapped. That's why he didn't leave us a note.''

Sam rose to his feet, shoved his hands into his pants pockets and walked to the window, his emotions warring inside over the guilt he'd hauled around for twenty years and the logical reasoning of his mother's words. Was she right? Had something just snapped?

A part of him desperately needed to believe her, but there was another part of him that was running scared. He finally gave voice to the question that had been tormenting him for weeks. ''Do you think his problems are genetic?''

Abigail came to his side, wrapped her arm around his waist and leaned her head against his shoulder. ''I'm not a doctor, so I can't say yes or no. But I am your mother, and I know you well enough to say that if it is, you haven't inherited the weakness. You'd no more take your life than I would, Sam. I know that in my heart, and a mother's heart never lies.''

''You're wonderful, did you know that?'' he asked as he wrapped his arm around her shoulders and gave her a squeeze. ''I know I don't say it often enough, but I love you.''

She gave him a trembling smile. ''I love you, too, so let's put the past behind us and start looking toward the future, starting with breakfast.''

''My taste buds are already salivating.''

Abigail chuckled. ''You always were too nice for your own good. Thankfully, you also have a steel-lined stomach.''

As she left his side, Sam returned his attention to the window, his mind involuntarily turning toward Liana. Desire surged through him at the memory of her voice, husky from sleep, when she'd answered the telephone this morning. He'd automatically conjured up a picture of her in bed that his libido had definitely approved of, and he reluctantly admitted that his feelings for her were more than infatuation. He was falling in love with her, and he was falling fast and hard.

That worried him, because after Kay had left him, he'd vowed that he'd never take a chance on love again. It hurt too much to love and lose. But could he really walk away from Liana, and if he didn't, was he strong enough to handle the rejection if she didn't want him?

He didn't know, and, thankfully, he was going to have a few days to contemplate the situation.

Chapter Ten

"Adriane, what in the world are you doing?" Liana screeched as she came barreling out of her bedroom when every fire alarm she had in the place went off.

"Exactly what you told me to do!" Adriane screeched back. "Watching the steaks."

Liana fought her way through the smoke to the stove and hauled out the broiler pan. She cursed beneath her breath when she realized that nearly ten dollars worth of steak had just been cremated.

"Open some windows," she instructed her sister. "I have to turn off the darn smoke alarms."

"Well, don't sound so grumpy!" Adriane yelled over the noise of the alarm as she walked across the room and began to open the windows. "It's not my fault."

"Of course, it's your faut!" Liana yelled back. "Why didn't you take the steaks out when they were done?"

"You didn't tell me to take them out, and how as I supposed to know when they're done? I've never broiled a steak before."

"Didn't it dawn on you that when smoke was pouring out of the oven something was wrong?"

"I thought it was supposed to do that. Grills smoke, don't they?"

"We weren't grilling!"

The open windows had cleared out enough smoke that the alarms automatically shut off, and Liana flinched when her last sentence came out in a bellow.

Adriane's face crumpled and her eyes filled with tears. "I was trying to do my best."

"Oh, Adriane, don't cry," Liana said with a heavy sigh as she went to her sister and hugged her. "I know you were trying to do your best, but when are you going to learn some common sense? Have you ever seen smoke come billowing out of the kitchen at home?"

"No, but you know how Cook is. She won't let anyone in the kitchen, so as far as I know, the place could be on fire half the time." She sniffed and swiped at her eyes. "Now, I've ruined dinner and we're going to starve to death, because we're snowed in, and even if we weren't, you don't have a car, and—"

"We won't starve," Liana interrupted as she led Adriane to the booth and forced her down into the seat. "I have enough soup to keep us alive for months. Would you prefer chicken noodle or chicken noodle?"

Adriane looked up at her and giggled. "That's a tough choice."

"Hey, life is tough."

"You know, I envy you," Adriane confined. "You're so together."

"Me?" Liana said in disbelief as she slid into the booth across from her. "Good heavens, I'm organized, but I'm not even close to being together. Now, I could see you saying that about Sandy. He's *together*."

Adriane groaned. "He's so together that he's obnoxious! Do you know that he actually sent away for applications to every Ivy League college the day that Junior was born? He said that you couldn't get started too early."

"Melanie finally had the baby?"

"Yeah. Last Monday, and he is the cutest thing, Liana. I hate to say it, but he looks exactly like Sandy, except he has Melanie's black hair. It's really thick and it stands up on end."

Adriane laughed delightedly before continuing, "Sandy wanted to take a picture of him, but he said he wasn't going to take one with the kid looking like a scarecrow. He told Melanie that he was going to grease his hair down with Vaseline, and she had him thrown out of the hospital! Boy, was he mad!"

"I bet he was," Liana murmured, experiencing a shaft of regret and a terrible pang of homesickness. She'd been an aunt for nearly a week and hadn't even known it. "They didn't really name him Henry Terrance Steven VII?"

"They did, and isn't it awful? The minute I heard that, I told everyone I was glad I was a girl. Not too many women name their progeny after themselves, and I can't think of anything more demoralizing than having the name of one of your parents. In fact, that's one of my boyfriend's biggest gripes. His father is Bob, and he's Bobby. It's really hard for him to make his family give him any respect, and he says it will be that way until the day he dies because he'll always be Bobby in their eyes."

"I didn't know you had a boyfriend," Liana stated. "Is it serious?"

Adriane blushed and glanced down at the tabletop. "Serious enough that I'm on birth control. And I don't want any lectures," she added as she jerked her head up. "We're responsible."

"I'm glad to hear that. Do Mom and Dad know about this?"

"About Bob yes. About birth control, no. As far as they're concerned, I should still be in diapers and bibs. I think they'd have a stroke or a heart attack if they found out that I was involved in a sexual relationship."

Liana raked her hand through her hair. Adriane was twenty years old and she didn't want to give her a lecture on sex, but she still felt obligated to offer a measure of advice. After all, wasn't that what big sisters were for?

"I don't want you to take this wrong, Adriane, but sex isn't something you can indulge in casually anymore. It's very important that you not only know your partner, but that you're aware of his . . . habits."

"Bob and I were both virgins, and we're not at risk, Liana. I may lack common sense, but I'm not stupid."

"Again, I'm glad to hear that," Liana replied with an inward sigh of relief. "So, what does your Bob think about your joining the Marine Corps?"

"He's not happy about it, but as I told him, I'm doing this for me and no one else. If what we have is love, it will last. If it doesn't, then it wasn't love in the first place, right?"

"Right," Liana said as she reached across the table and caught Adriane's hand. "You know, I never thought I'd say this, but I'm glad you've come. You're my little sister, and because you are, I love you, but I don't think I've ever thought of you as a person before. I also have to say that I really like that person."

"Even if I do burn up steaks?"

"Especially because you burn up steaks," Liana answered with a soft laugh. "So, should we go to work on that soup?"

"I don't know," Adriane said with a melodramatic sigh. "There are so many choices that I can't possibly see us making up our mind. The news said that the roads are finally open. How would you feel about ordering a pizza? It would be my treat, of course."

"Who am I to complain if you're treating?"

WHEN LIANA OPENED THE DOOR thirty minutes later expecting the pizza delivery person, she found Sam instead.

"What are you doing here?" she asked in surprise.

"Returning your car." He stomped the snow off his boots, stepped inside and handed her her keys. "It's running like a top, but you should get a complete tune-up in a few months. Where's Adriane?"

"In the guest room watching television," Liana answered as she closed the door.

"I thought you didn't own a television."

"I don't. Through the miracle of credit cards, she rented one and had it delivered. I can't stand the noise, so I made her put it in her room."

"I'm glad," Sam said huskily.

"Why?" she asked in confusion.

"Because if she wasn't watching television in her room, I couldn't do this."

Before Liana knew what was happening, he pulled her into his arms and kissed her.

She'd told herself that she wasn't going to let him do this to her, but the moment his lips touched hers she was lost. She pressed the palms of her hands against his chilled cheeks, which were in direct contrast to his warm tongue as he teased at her lips, forcing them to part. She put up a token struggle by refusing to comply, but when he pulled her hips to his and she felt the stirring of his manhood, she let him have his way. The kiss seemed to go on forever, and it was so wonderful that she was actually hearing bells.

She didn't realize it was the doorbell until Adriane muttered, "Would you two please break it up and get out of the way before the pizza man leaves? I'm starving."

Liana would have leaped away from Sam in embarrassment, but he had his arms linked securely around her waist and held her in place.

He chuckled softly when a blush flooded her cheeks, and then he looked at Adriane and said, "I'll get out of the way if I'm invited for dinner."

"Then, consider yourself invited," the girl grumbled.

"Thanks," Sam said, finally releasing Liana.

While Adriane took care of the pizza and Sam hung up his coat, Liana fled to the kitchen. She knew it was ridiculous to be embarrassed by the fact that Adriane had caught her in a clinch with Sam. After all, the girl had already confided her own escapades in that area, but she was still her baby sister, and baby sisters weren't supposed to find big sisters in compromising positions.

She pulled out the coffeemaker and started making coffee for Sam. Then she gathered plates and silverware and set them on the counter.

"Don't bother setting me a place," Adriane said as she walked into the room and dropped the pizza box down next to the plates. "There's a *Star Trek* festival on, and I'm going to be holed up in my room for the rest of the night."

"Adriane, that's rude," Liana chided. "You can't invite Sam to dinner and then go to your room and watch TV."

"I didn't invite him to dinner, he invited himself." She glanced toward the doorway where Sam was standing and winked at him. "Besides, after what I just saw in the living room, I think it would be even ruder for me to stay."

"Adriane!"

"What?" the girl said, widening her eyes innocently as she grabbed one of the plates and popped open the lid of the pizza box.

"Apologize for that crack, and apologize this instant," Liana ordered.

"Sure. Sorry." But she didn't look the least bit contrite. She filled her plate, grabbed a couple cans of soda out of the refrigerator and said, "Ta, ta. You two lovebirds have fun. I'll see you in the morning, Liana. You, too, Sam, if you play your cards right. Good luck."

"Adriane!" But the girl had already disappeared. "I'm going to strangle her. I swear, I'm going to strangle her," Liana muttered furiously.

"You can do that later," Sam said as he walked to her, linked an arm around her waist and pulled her back against him. "Now, where were we before we were so rudely interrupted by the pizza man?"

"Sam, we can't do this."

"Why? Because Adriane's in the house?"

"It has nothing to do with Adriane, and you know it," she said as she put her hand against his chest and pushed. Thankfully, he released her, because she had the feeling that if he hadn't, she wouldn't have been able to budge him an inch.

"I suppose you're referring to our little tiff yesterday," he said as she carried the box of pizza to the booth and sat down.

"That wasn't a tiff," she replied, helping herself to a slice of pizza. "It was a serious difference of opinion."

"Which opinion are you referring to?" he questioned as he slid in across from her and reached for the pizza. "The fact that I think you need to face your feelings, or the fact that I'm going to continue to pursue you regardless of what you do."

"Both," Liana stated staunchly. "My life is my life, Sam, and no one has a right to interfere in it. I think we should agree to disagree and go back to an employee-employer relationship."

He leaned back in his seat and laughed. "If you believe we can do that, you're in need of more help than I thought."

"This is not a laughing matter, Sam. I'm completely serious. I can't get involved with you. I *won't* get involved with you. What happened yesterday was a mistake."

"Maybe it was a mistake, but it happened. It was also the most wonderful experience of my life, and you don't walk away from wonderful, Liana. I am going to pursue you, whether you like it or not."

Liana threw her pizza down, leaped up from the booth and walked to the back door before turning around to face him. "Why are you doing this to me?" she asked plaintively. "Please, Sam, if you have any respect for me at all, then agree to go back to a business relationship."

Sam went to her, hooked his finger beneath her chin and raised her head. Her eyes were filled with tears, and it suddenly dawned on him that he'd never actually seen her cry. Even yesterday when she'd been a mass of terrified quivering flesh in his arms and he'd heard the rasp of tears in each breath she'd heaved into her lungs, she'd never shed a one.

"My decision has nothing to do with respect, Liana. What's sparking between us is powerful, and I don't think we can fight against it and win. I honestly believe that the only way we can deal with it is to just go with it and see what happens."

"But I can't do that!" she exclaimed vehemently.

"Why? What's the worst that could happen? Talk to me, Liana. For once, talk to me and tell me what's going on inside you. What is the very worst that could happen if you ride it out?"

"I could fall in love with you, and I can't do that, Sam. I *won't* do it!"

Her words were like a knife wound, and Sam nearly doubled over from the pain. What was it about him that precluded those people he loved from loving him back? And, as he'd already admitted to himself today, he was falling in love with Liana.

Maybe she was right. Maybe they should go back to the way things were. Hell, he'd already given his grandfather enough pictures to perk him up, so maybe he should walk away before he really got hurt. But Sam knew he couldn't do that. He knew that if he walked away he'd always wonder about what might have been if he'd just taken a chance.

"It's going to be all right," he said as he drew her head to his shoulder. "It will be all right, Liana, because I refuse to let it be any other way."

"How can you be so strong?" she whispered.

Because I don't have a choice, he answered inwardly. Aloud, he said, "Hey, it's a tough job, but someone has to do it."

LIANA SHOT UP IN BED to escape the nightmare, but at least this time she wasn't screaming. She also knew that she wasn't because this nightmare had been different. In it Sam had been staring at her with the same horror in his eyes that she'd seen in her parents'. He'd been repelled by her, and he'd walked away from her in disgust.

And that's what was going to happen if she didn't keep her distance from him, she told herself. She'd end up loving him and he'd end up hating her.

She wanted to cry. Lord, she wanted to cry, but the tears wouldn't come. No matter how hard she willed them, they just wouldn't come.

"LIANA COME HERE! QUICK!" Adriane squealed.

"What's wrong?" Liana asked as she hurried into the living room.

Adriane pointed out the front window. "Nothing's wrong. Just look outside."

Liana's mouth dropped open in disbelief when she looked out the window and found herself staring at the biggest snowman she'd ever seen in her life.

"When did you do that?" she asked her sister.

"I didn't do it. You know I hate snow."

"But if you didn't, then who did?"

"Hooligan?"

"Very funny."

Adriane propped her elbows on the windowsill. "You know, it looks as if he's holding a note, doesn't it?"

"Yeah, it does. Why don't you go out and see what it says?"

"It's your front yard. You go see what it says."

Liana started to argue, but realized Adriane did have a point. She pulled on her parka and boots and walked out to the snowman. He was, indeed, holding a note and Liana frowned when she read: "Watch your backside."

"What in the world is that supposed to mean?" she muttered and then let out a yelp when a snowball hit her in the middle of the back.

She spun around to see Sam standing at the edge of her house, a mischievous grin on his face as he threw another snowball at her. She ducked behind the snowman to keep from being hit, trying to decide if she should be angry with him or if she should laugh.

The laughter won out and she grabbed a handful of snow, yelling, "If it's war you want, Sam Dillon, then it's war you've got."

With that she leaped out from behind the snowman and fired her missile, hitting him in the face.

"Hey, that's a foul!" he exclaimed. "The rules say no snowballs above the neck."

"Yeah, well I don't play fair," she said as she threw another one at him.

He dropped into a crouch and Liana realized too late that he'd built up a good supply of snowballs. He began to fire them at her in rapid succession, and she started laughing so hard as they pummeled against her that she couldn't even find the strength to get back behind the snowman to protect herself.

"You are so beautiful when you laugh," Sam told her when he walked up to her and pulled her into his arms. "You should do it more often." He regretted the words the instant they were out of his mouth, because Liana immediately sobered and tried to pull away from him.

He tightened his hold around her when she said, "Let me go, Sam."

"No. You're not going to withdraw from me, Liana."

She stared up at him, her lips pursed in a mutinous line. "Just what do you think you're trying to prove?"

"That somewhere inside that gorgeous body of yours exists a fun person who can laugh and have as much fun as the next guy."

"I'm not supposed to have fun."

"Why not?"

"Because I'm not."

"Tough. You're going to have some anyway," Sam muttered.

Before Liana knew what was happening, he leaned down, hefted her over his shoulder and walked across the yard.

"Sam Dillon, you put me down right this instant!" she bellowed.

"Okay." He dropped her flat on her back in the middle of a snowdrift.

Liana let out a screech of outrage and leaped to her feet, her hands balled into fists at her sides. "How dare you do that to me!"

He shrugged. "You told me to put you down."

"I didn't mean that way, and you know it!"

"Well, let's try it again and see if I can do it right this time."

"Don't you come near me," Liana said as she backed away from him. "I mean it, Sam," she added when he advanced on her.

"Sorry, but I never did respond well to orders."

"Why are you doing this to me?" she asked in frustration.

"Because I am."

"That's no answer!"

His lips lifted in a wry smile. "I know."

"You're making me angry, Sam."

"Good."

"Good? You want to make me mad?"

"Sure. At least it's an honest emotion."

Liana jumped in startled surprise when she backed into her fence. Sam was right in front of her, and she knew she was trapped. He braced a hand on either side of her head and lowered his face so that they were at eye level.

"Well, I'm waiting," he drawled.

"For what?" she asked warily.

"You tell me."

She glared at him and wanted to kick him in the shin when all he did was smile in return.

"I don't know what you want from me," she finally muttered.

"Liar," he murmured and then kissed her.

"Sam, please don't," she whispered when he released her lips.

"Why not?"

"Because."

"That's not an answer."

"I know, but . . ."

"But?"

When she didn't respond, he kissed her again, and Liana groaned as desire surged through her with such force that her knees weakened. She was sure she would have slid right down to the ground if Sam hadn't chosen that moment to pull her against him, and the moment their bodies connected, she knew that if he'd been trying to get an honest emotion out of her, he'd succeeded. She wanted him so badly that she thought she might die from the need.

She kept telling herself that she couldn't do this. She kept telling herself that she'd succumbed once and everything had backfired on her. She had to pull away from him. She had to put them back on a business level. She had to . . .

"Sam?" she asked with a throaty sigh.

"Mmmmm?" he hummed lazily.

"Take me to your place so we can make love."

"I thought you said you weren't supposed to have fun."

"Tough. I'm going to have some anyway."

Sam laughed as he bent and tossed her back over his shoulder and strode toward his car.

"Sam!" Liana exclaimed as they passed her front window and Adriane waved at her, a wide grin on her face. "You're making a scene. What is my sister going to think?"

"That I've finally played my cards right," he said as he fondly patted her bottom before opening the car door and dropping her onto the seat.

She parted her lips to scold him, but he stopped her by kissing her. It was such a long, deep kiss that she was on fire by the time he finally pulled away, and the hungry glint in his eyes fanned the flame.

She reached up and touched his face as her heart expanded and contracted with a feeling of such deep emotion that she didn't even want to name it. She only wanted to savor it, and then she'd tuck it away and cherish it forever.

Chapter Eleven

Sam shivered in pleasure and blushed right to the roots of his hair as Liana touched him intimately and whispered huskily, "Do you like that?"

Thank heavens, he knew she didn't expect him to answer, because he couldn't have even gotten out a growl. When Liana had said she wanted to make love to him, he hadn't realized it was going to be like this, and it suddenly hit Sam that in fifteen years of marriage, Kay had never once made love to him. Sure, she'd been the aggressor on occasion, but she'd never come close to doing anything like this, and he was both ecstatic and shy about Liana's ministrations.

Liana wasn't shy, though. She was fascinated by Sam. In her six years as a professional photographer, she'd photographed people, places and animals so beautiful that they took one's breath away, but she had never in her life seen anything as beautiful as Sam. She couldn't look at him enough. She couldn't touch him enough. The hair on his body was both smooth and bristly, depending where she touched, and Sam shifted restlessly beneath her hands as she explored the many textures of his body.

"Don't move," she ordered throatily. "Relax, Sam. Just relax and let me love you."

She had to be kidding! Sam thought, his body jerking involuntarily when she leaned over his chest, first her hair trailing across it and then her lips and tongue touching his breast. His housekeeper cursed his brass bedstead every time she had to polish it, but he blessed it as he reached over his head and clasped two of the ornate rods, knowing that if he didn't hold onto something, he was going to fly apart.

He'd never been this aroused, and a part of him wanted to scream at Liana to hurry up and get this exquisite torture over with, while another part wanted to beg her never to let it end.

Finally, it was more than he could bear, and he whispered harshly, "Now, Liana. Please, now."

She met his gaze and smiled, and Sam gulped. He'd never seen a woman look so...lustful.

"Now?" she repeated so softly, so sensuously, that gooseflesh sprang up on his body, and he could only nod. "Okay, but you can't touch me and you can't move. Promise me you won't touch me and you won't move."

She had to be crazy! There was no way he could keep from touching her or moving. No way.

But when she said, "Promise?" he nodded again.

His grip on the bedstead tightened, and he had to close his eyes and grit his teeth to keep from reaching for her as she straddled his hips and slowly lowered herself onto him. Instinct made him flex his hips to surge into her, but he froze when she exclaimed lowly, "Don't move!"

He knew he was going to die, because the effort to keep his promise to her had him holding his breath, and his heart was galloping so fast he couldn't tell one beat from the next. But just when he was certain that this was the end, she took him completely and began to move over him in a swaying rhythm that sent him rushing toward a climax.

"I can't wait!" he cried out hoarsely.

"You don't have to," Liana whispered as she lowered her lips to his. "I'm right there with you, Sam."

And then she kissed him so passionately that Sam knew she was telling him the truth and he let himself go.

SAM HAD NO IDEA how much time had elapsed when the world finally began to right itself, and he released his hold on the bedstead and hugged Liana, who was sprawled over him.

"No one's ever done anything like that to me before," he stated quietly as he began to stroke her hair.

She raised her head and smiled at him. "I've never done anything like that to anyone before. I've never *wanted* to do anything like that to anyone before, but you're such a special man and I wanted to do something extra special for you."

Her confession brought tears to Sam's eyes and made his heart fill to the point of bursting. He was in love with her, he admitted, and he wanted to tell her. Hell, he wanted to shout it to the world, but he knew he couldn't. Not until he knew she loved him back. If he handed her his heart and she cast it aside, he knew it would destroy him.

"What are you thinking?" Liana asked as she trailed a finger down his temple.

Sam rolled her to his side and pressed a kiss to her forehead. "I was thinking that you're pretty special yourself."

Liana started to object, but decided to hold her peace. She was too content right now to get into a sparring match with him, and she stretched luxuriously against him when he ran his hand down her back in long relaxing strokes. She was just going to lie there and enjoy it. Her eyelids dropped, and she forced them back open, telling herself that she wasn't going to fall asleep. She couldn't let herself fall asleep. But soon Sam's stroking hand lulled her into further drowsiness and she slipped off without even realizing it.

Sam, however, couldn't sleep, and he knew it was because he was expecting Liana to wake up screaming from another nightmare. As he lay beside her, watching her face for any sign of distress, he recalled how wonderful she'd looked today when she'd been laughing in uproarious pleasure. He also recalled how he'd destroyed that happy mood, and he knew it was time he finally found out what was going on with her.

While he continued to watch her sleep, he began to formulate a plan that might let him slip through her walls of defense and get some answers, and he was surprised when Liana opened her eyes and smiled at him. He hadn't realized she was awakening, and he was relieved that there had been no nightmare.

"What are you doing?" she asked sleepily.

"Watching you sleep," he answered.

"Sounds boring."

He gave her a teasing smile. "Well, into every man's life a little boredom must fall."

She chuckled and ran her hand over his shoulder and down his chest. "Maybe we should liven things up."

"Maybe."

"Any suggestions on how we could do that?" she asked suggestively.

"There is something I really want to do," he murmured as he cuddled her against him, deciding that now was as good a time as any to put his plan into action.

"And, pray tell, what might that be?" she asked with a flirtatious bat of her lashes.

"I want to talk."

Her eyes flew wide and then narrowed suspiciously. "About what?"

He shrugged. "The vagaries of life. World politics. You."

"I think it's time for me to leave," she said, rolling away from him.

"No, it's not." He caught her around the waist and pulled her back to him. "Just bear with me, Liana. I only want to chitchat."

Liana frowned, because she didn't believe him for one second. Sam was a tenacious man and she wouldn't put it past him to talk her right into a trap. That meant she was going to have to remain on her toes.

"What is it you want to know about me?" she asked warily.

"Your favorite color."

"My favorite color?" He nodded, and she said, "I've never really given it much thought, but blue, I guess."

"Cool blue or hot blue?"

"I didn't know it came in temperatures."

He chucked her under the chin. "Humor me. Do you prefer a cool ice-blue or a hot sapphire-blue?"

"Sapphire. What's your favorite color?"

"Oh, no, you don't," he chided good-naturedly. "This is my game, and you aren't going to turn the conversation around on me. What's your favorite food?"

"Beef stroganoff."

"Now, you're getting the hang of it. What's your favorite sport?"

"Tennis."

Sam smiled as he felt her begin to relax against him. So far the plan was working well. "Favorite movie?"

"You'll laugh."

"That's okay. Tell me anyway."

"*Bambi*."

He chuckled. "What's your favorite book?"

"*Gone with the Wind*."

"Flower?"

"Daffodil."

"Type of music?"

"It's a toss-up between soft rock and Beethoven."

"Have you ever been married?"

She went rigid in his arms, and Sam knew he'd hit pay dirt. Only as he lay there watching her sleep had it dawned on him that though they'd discussed his marital history, they'd never discussed hers.

"Have you been married, Liana?" he pressed when she didn't answer.

"No," she said woodenly and tried to roll away from him again.

But Sam was prepared for that reaction and held her in place. "Engaged?"

"I'm tired of this game. Let me up, Sam."

"Not until you answer my last question."

"I was engaged once, all right?" she stated furiously as she shoved ineffectually against his chest. "Now, let me up!"

He rolled so that she was trapped beneath him. "One more question, and then I'll let you up."

"You said that when you asked the last question," she pointed out as she glared at him.

"So, I lied last time, but I give you my word that this is the very last question I'll ask you today. Answer it and I'll let you up. Why didn't you get married?"

He'd been prepared for everything from fury to tears, and he could only stare in disbelief when he watched her eyes, which had been so alive only a moment ago, fade into nothing. The most disconcerting part was that she hadn't even closed them. It wasn't that he hadn't seen her this way before that upset him, because, of course, he had. But it had been so long since he'd seen her like this that he'd forgotten how unsettling it was.

"Liana?" he questioned in concern as he stroked her hair away from her face.

She drew in a long, shuddering breath and said, "My fiance died. Now, I've answered your question, so please let me up. I want to go home."

At this point, the very last thing Sam wanted to do was let her up. Her response had given life to a million more questions, but he'd given her his word that he wouldn't ask any more today, and he knew she'd never trust him if he reneged on it.

Reluctantly, he released her and watched her get out of bed and begin to dress. Even her movements were different now, he noted. They were stilted, even jerky at times, as if she were a puppet and the puppeteer didn't quite have control over the strings.

When she finished dressing she walked out of the room without a word or a glance, and Sam couldn't decide if he wanted to curse or to throw something, so he decided to get up and get dressed instead.

LIANA SAT ON SAM'S SOFA and willed herself into oblivion. She had to go back to that nice, safe world where she used to live and didn't have to feel. She didn't want to feel. She wasn't going to feel. She . . .

Damn Sam and his parody of Twenty Questions! she thought as her temper flared. She'd known it was a trick. She'd told herself she had to remain on her toes, so why had she relaxed? If she just hadn't relaxed she would have been on-guard instead of caught so off-guard and could have hidden her reaction from him.

A tremor of fear shook her, because she knew that Sam was close to finding out the truth. He was so damn close. If she didn't stop seeing him, he was going to learn everything, and she knew it as certainly as she knew that Adriane would do something maddening between now and tomorrow.

She had to walk away from him today and never see him again, but if she did that, she'd not only lose Neal's business, she'd put him in a financial lurch. He was planning on the business being sold before he left and he needed the money. She supposed she could ask her parents for the money. She didn't want to, but she could, so maybe the business wouldn't be a problem after all.

However, there were still Sam's photographs to consider, and that was a dilemma. They were a special gift for his grandfather, and he adored the old man. He wasn't going to have him much longer, and she knew intuitively that when his grandfather died, it was going to devastate him. Could she really steal the memory of that special gift away from him? Could she live with herself if she did?

No, she couldn't, which meant that if she couldn't line up another photographer in the next few days, she was going to have to take them. She also knew that finding a good photographer on such short notice was going to be next to impossible, despite the money Sam was willing to pay. Their schedules were usually booked months in advance.

So, she was stuck, and she might as well resign herself to that fact. All she could do was keep her guard up and Sam at arm's length, and she might be able to escape this mess unscathed.

Except that wasn't quite true, because Liana knew that if she wasn't in love with Sam, she was so darn close to it that it was going to hurt like hell when he finally walked away. Tears filled her eyes and she blinked against them. When Sam came out of the bedroom, she couldn't have tears in her eyes. She had to be completely in control. Completely.

THE MINUTE SAM WALKED into the living room, Liana bounded off the sofa and headed for the door, saying, "I want to go home."

Sam's temper erupted. Why did she keep running away from him? Why wouldn't she let him help her? If she'd only talk to him, he knew he could help her, and, by damn if he was good enough to sleep with, then he was good enough to confide in.

He caught her arm and made her turn around to face him. "You're not going anywhere until we've talked."

"Let go of me!" she spat at him.

Sam released her arm and stepped back from her. At least she didn't look empty now, and he far preferred her fury to that blank face.

He tucked his hands into his back pockets as he said, "Liana, I know I hit a nerve in there, and I'm sorry if I hurt you. But I care about you. I care about you a lot. All I want you to do is talk to me. Please, tell me what you're feeling."

Liana looked up at him and shook her head. How could she possibly tell a man like Sam that she was feeling terror and self-hatred and guilt because she had killed the man she loved?

"I can't tell you what I'm feeling, Sam, so please just leave it alone," she pleaded.

"I care too much about you to do that, Liana," he said with a heavy sigh as he reached out and caught the back of her head in his hand, guiding her into his arms. He sighed and rested his cheek against her hair as he cradled her against him. "You have to deal with your feelings. It's the only way you can put this emotional season of winter behind you. Life is so damn short, honey, but it is one hell of a long and bumpy ride if you're miserable."

"Some people deserve to be miserable, and I'm one of them," she said as she raised her head and gazed up at him through tear-washed eyes. "If I give you what you want, you're going to hate me."

Sam caught her face between his hands and stared deeply into her eyes, willing her to trust him. God, he needed her to trust him. "I could never hate you, Liana. Never."

"That's easy for you to say now, because you don't know what I am or what I've done. If you found out, you would hate me. I know it. It's bad enough that I hate myself, and I couldn't stand it if you hated me, too. So, please take me home and stop pursuing me. All you're doing is wasting your time and making us both miserable."

Sam wanted to pull his hair and scream like a banshee in frustration. He wasn't going to stop pursuing her. He was in love with her, and he was going to help her if it was the last thing he ever did. But how could he help her if he couldn't find out what was going on?

What would his grandfather do in a situation like this? he asked himself. Take her up to the mountains, but the snow precluded Sam from doing that. At this time of year, a new snowfall was an avalanche waiting to happen. He wouldn't take her into the mountains again until he knew for certain it was safe, and that would be another three or four days.

But he had to do something, and he had to do it now, because gut instinct told him that if he let Liana walk out the door, he was going to lose her. She'd crawl back into that empty shell she'd been in when he first met her, and he'd never get her out again.

His gaze flew around the apartment looking for anything that would give him an idea, but his mind remained blank. Finally, he returned his gaze to her face. She was watching him, her eyes still filled with tears, and it hit him again that he'd never seen her cry. The last time he'd cried was when he was ten years old, and he knew firsthand how badly it hurt to keep all those tears bottled up inside.

And from out of the clear blue sky, it struck him that that was the solution. If he could get her to cry, she couldn't crawl back into that shell. She'd have to start facing her feelings, and when she did, maybe she'd start trusting him enough to talk.

"I'll take you home, but I need your help with something first."

Liana's self-protective radar switched on. What was he up to now? And she knew he was up to something. He had that determined look on his face that said: Look out mountain, here I come.

"I don't want to play any more games, Sam. I want to go home. If you won't take me home, then I'll call a cab."

"This isn't a game. I need your help."

"Doing what?" she asked suspiciously.

"We're having a big potluck dinner at the office tomorrow, and I'm supposed to bring the chili," he lied cheerfully. "I make a great homemade chili, but I should have started it hours ago. Since it's your fault that I didn't," he said with a suggestive leer, "the least you can do is help me get it started."

"You want me to help you make chili?"

He nodded.

"And that's it."

He held his hand up in a Boy Scout salute. "Scout's honor."

Liana still didn't trust him, but she supposed she could go along with him for now. But this time, she'd remain on her toes. He was not going to catch her off-guard again.

"All right, I'll help."

"Good."

She followed him to the kitchen, where he told her, "Sit down at the breakfast counter. While I pull everything else together, you can chop the onions, okay?"

"Sure," Liana answered as she slid onto one of the stools.

"Great, that will save me tons of time."

He placed a chopping block and a knife in front of her. Then he retrieved a bag of onions from one of his bottom cupboards and dropped it beside the chopping block.

"How many of them do you need?" she asked as she opened the bag and pulled out a couple of onions.

"All of them," he answered.

Liana gaped at him in disbelief. "All of them? There must be twenty onions here. That's enough onions to make chili for an army!"

"I am making chili for an army. I have sixty employees and they eat like a hundred and sixty, so start chopping, Liana. The sooner you're done, the sooner I can take you home."

He began whistling as he turned away from her, and Liana's radar perked up significantly. She regarded him warily, more certain than ever that he was up to something, but unable to figure out what. When he pulled out three huge stew pots and a frying pan, she relaxed somewhat. It appeared that he really was making chili for an army, and since it wasn't normal to have that many large stew pots in one kitchen, he must have done it before.

With a shrug, she began her task. As he said, the sooner she was done, the sooner she could go home, and then she wouldn't have to worry about keeping up her guard.

Sam watched Liana out of the corner of his eye as he went through the motions of getting all the ingredients he'd need to make chili. He began to wonder if his plan was going to work when she finished off the third onion, but by the end of the fourth onion, she began to sniff and he crowed inwardly in triumph.

Come on, sweetheart, swipe at the beautiful little nose, he encouraged silently. *You need a good whiff of that smelly onion juice.*

Almost as if on command, she swiped at her nose with the back of her hand and then closed her eyes and shook her head in distaste. By the end of the sixth onion she was sniffing continually and blinking almost nonstop. It took another three onions before Sam saw the first tear roll onto her lashes. He held his breath as he watched it hover for what seemed like forever before it finally rolled down her cheek, and Sam made a bet with himself. By the twelfth onion she'd be putting out more water than a faucet. He lost the bet, but he didn't care, because onion thirteen was the clincher. She went through two more onions before the first sob came out, and Sam knew the dam had finally burst.

He hurried to her and lifted her into his arms. She buried her head against his chest and cried so brokenly that it made his heart ache. Cradling her with the same tenderness as a child, he carried her into his bedroom and tucked her into bed. It was difficult but he resisted the desperate need to crawl in with her and hold her tight, because he knew that this type of crying jag had to be indulged in alone.

He pressed a kiss against her forehead and whispered, "You'll be all right now, Liana. You're going to be just fine."

Then he walked out of the room, quietly closing the door behind him.

LIANA OPENED HER EYES as the illuminated dial on Sam's alarm clock switched to 2:00. The darkness in the room told her it was the middle of the night, and she rolled to her back and blinked at the ceiling. Her eyes were scratchy, her throat was raw and her head ached, but she felt better than she had in years.

Finding that realization puzzling, she slowly prodded at her feelings. It was as if something had changed inside her, and at first she couldn't figure what it was. Then it occurred to her that that terrible feeling of terror she'd been dragging around with her for three years was gone. There wasn't even one twinge of it left.

Slowly, she sat up in bed and glanced around, half expecting to find Sam lurking in the shadows, but he wasn't. She wondered if he knew how much that meant to her, and then understood that he did. Falling apart was embarrassing enough without having someone witness it. If he hadn't understood her need for privacy, he would have stayed, because Sam was not a man who would normally leave a crying woman alone.

She climbed out of bed and went into the bathroom. When she flipped on the light, she studied her image in the mirror. Her face showed all the ravages of a good cry, and yet it, too, had somehow changed. It looked more…serene was the only word she could come up with, and she did feel more serene. But why?

Again, she slowly examined her feelings and was amazed to see new tears appear and roll down her cheeks, and she understood that this strange feeling of serenity was because she could cry. She'd been trying to cry ever since the day of Bill's death, but the tears would never come. No matter how hard she'd willed them, they wouldn't come. It was as if she'd been given a miracle.

And she had been given one, she thought as more tears began to fall. His name was Samuel Quinten Dillon, and he was the most wonderful man in the world. She'd bet her bottom dollar that if she walked out to the kitchen there wouldn't be one pot of chili. Somehow he'd known that she needed to cry, and he'd made her cut up onions so she could.

It was then that Liana admitted that she loved him with all her heart, and she always would. The tears began to fall harder when she also admitted that no matter how much she loved him, she could never have him. He may have dragged her out of her nightmare, but he couldn't change what had happened.

She would, however, have a couple more weeks with him. She'd take the most beautiful pictures possible for his grandfather, and she'd spend her time with Sam creating enough memories to carry her through a lifetime.

She wet a washrag and washed her face, but she didn't do anything about the swelling around her eyes. It was reassuring to have the proof that she could cry again, and she wanted to hold on to that proof for a while.

When she was done, she went looking for Sam, because she knew it was time they talked.

Chapter Twelve

Sam had dozed off on the sofa, but he was instantly awake the moment he heard the water running in the bathroom.

He sat up, looked at his watch and calculated the time. Nearly ten hours had passed since he'd tucked Liana into bed, and they had been the most agonizing ten hours of his life. Twice he'd peeked in on her, the first time after her heart-wrenching sobbing had finally stopped, confirming that she'd cried herself to sleep; then, again, a few hours ago, to make sure she was resting peacefully.

But if the past ten hours had been agonizing, the minutes that ticked by after she turned off the water were excruciating, and Sam had to force himself not to go charging into the bedroom to check on her.

Had he done the right thing by forcing her into tears? At the time it had seemed like the right thing to do, but when he'd sat here listening to her cry her heart out for nearly two hours, he'd begun to be plagued with doubt. If he'd put her through this and it hadn't helped, he didn't think he'd ever forgive himself.

His nerves were stretched so tightly in anticipation of the bedroom door opening that he jumped in surprise when it finally did, and he made himself sit still instead of rushing to her as he wanted to. He'd been so worried about her that he was afraid he'd squeeze the breath out of her if he touched her right now.

As she walked toward him, he searched her face, his heart twisting painfully at the sight of her poor, swollen eyes, but then she smiled at him. He sagged back against the cushions in relief. He had done the right thing.

His voice was rough with emotion when he asked, "How are you feeling?"

Her smile widened. "Hungry for chili."

She let out a delighted laugh when his cheeks flamed bright red and he gave a guilty duck of his head. "There is no chili," he confessed.

"I know."

She sat down beside him and took his hand in hers. "I've always thought you were a wonderful man, but today you showed me how wonderful you really are. Thank you, Sam. I'll be grateful to you for the rest of my life for this."

Sam swallowed hard. As had become the norm in his dealings with her, he felt torn by two emotions. One was happiness, for he was truly happy that he had helped her. But he was also hurt, because he didn't want her gratitude. He wanted her love, and he wanted it so badly that it was eating him up inside.

"I'm glad I was able to help," he told her gruffly.

"Well, you did help. And you were right. I had to face my feelings. Now that I have, I also know that we need to talk."

Hope does spring eternal, and it flared brightly inside Sam. If she was willing to talk, then maybe, just maybe, he hadn't been chasing rainbows. He held his breath as he waited for her to continue.

It seemed as if an eon had passed before she said, "You've been asking me to tell you what was going on inside me. I know now that it was terror, but I'm not sure if I was as terrified of the past as I was of your learning the truth about it. In your efforts to drag me out of my nightmare, as you so astutely called it, you were getting too close to discovering my secrets. I couldn't let you do that, because I knew you'd end up hating me.''

"I told you before, I could never hate you!" Sam told her passionately as he sat forward and gripped her hand tightly.

She gave him a sad smile. "Yes, you could, Sam, and believe me, you would. I..." She caught herself before she said love, and quickly changed it to, "...like you too much to let that happen, so after I finish taking your grandfather's pictures, I have to stop seeing you."

Sam felt the pain coming, and he knew it was going to be so intense he wouldn't be able to stand it. In defense, he let his temper take root and hold. She liked him too much? He worshiped the very ground on which she walked, and she *liked* him? Caring he could have handled, but *like*?

The first word that sprang to his lips in response to her words was a rude and explicit curse, and he barely managed to hold it back. He could actually taste its bitterness as he swallowed it, and he surged to his feet, then paced the room.

He wanted to scream at her. He wanted to rail at her. He wanted to shake her until her teeth rattled. Why was it that the people he loved could walk away from him so easily? What was wrong with him that let them do that? There had to be something wrong, but what the hell was it?

"Let me get this straight," he stated tautly. "You have some terrible secret in your past, and you want to stop seeing me, because if I find out what this secret is, I'm going to hate you."

"Yes," Liana replied softly as she watched him with growing concern. Since Sam had told her several times that he cared about her, she knew she was hurting him. But it was better to hurt him now than to let his caring deepen to love and then walk away from him. And she knew he didn't love her yet. If he did, he would have told her. He was too open with her to withhold those feelings from her.

"So the day you finish taking my grandfather's pictures, we're over. Finished, as in never to lay eyes on each other again."

"I'm sorry, Sam, but yes."

He stopped his pacing and assumed an aggressive stance with his feet planted apart and his thumbs hooked in the belt loops of his jeans. His eyes were brilliant with anger, and his voice was ice when he asked, "Until that happens, am I at least going to have bedroom privileges, or are you going to cut me off there, too?"

Liana flinched as the question hit her like a slap. But what did she expect? she asked herself morosely. This man had been so good to her, and she was paying him back by hurting him.

"No, Sam, you won't have bedroom privileges," she whispered, dropping her gaze to her hands to hide her regret. She knew that she could never make love with him again. If she did, she might not be able to walk away, and she loved him too much not to walk away.

"Get your coat," he ordered curtly. "It's time for you to go home."

They made the drive to her house in total silence, and when he pulled to a stop, she said, "Don't bother getting out, Sam. Give me a call when you're ready to go back into the mountains."

Sam nodded, because he knew that his voice would crack if he spoke. Now that the anger was fading, the pain was coming back, and he didn't want it to hit him here. If it did, he didn't know what he'd do. Hell, he didn't know what he was going to do anyway, but he didn't want it to happen here.

SAM WAS NOT ONLY SURPRISED but elated when he walked into his grandfather's room and noticed that he looked better than he had in months. He knew that the old man's seeming recovery was due to Liana's photographs. Spring had always revived him, and after seeing him like this, Sam became convinced that the doctors were wrong. His grandfather was *not* a hopeless case. His condition would continue to improve so he could have the heart surgery he needed. Sam knew he had to believe that, because he didn't know what he'd do without his grandfather around to give him his sage advice. He needed him so badly, because he was his only firm grip on life.

"Hi, Gramps. I'm glad you're up," he told him. "I need to talk to you. Boy, do I need to talk to you, but I don't know where to begin."

"The beginning is usually the best place to start," his grandfather stated.

"Yeah, but I'm not sure where the beginning begins."

He paced the room with his hands stuffed in his pockets to keep from resorting to an old childhood habit of biting his fingernails to the quick.

"If you're trying to impersonate a caged animal, you've managed it," his grandfather finally said with a soft laugh. "Why don't you sit down and tell me what's on your mind?"

Sam shook his head at the suggestion, knowing that he couldn't sit if he wanted to. He'd spent the last two days replaying Liana's conversation over and over in his mind, and even though he knew it was probably no more than wishful thinking, he kept hearing a slight hesitation in her voice before she'd said the word "like." Was it possible that she'd started to say love and caught herself in time? He wanted to believe that. He wanted to believe that so badly, but was he grasping at straws?

"I'm in love," he finally told his grandfather.

The old man gave a sage nod. "Figured as much. Only love could make you this miserable."

Sam gave the old man a wry smile. "Is there anything you don't know?"

His grandfather pursed his lips thoughtfully before shaking his head. "Not anything worthwhile knowing. A man's life is pretty simple, Sam. It's dictated by his emotions. The trick is not letting those emotions get out of hand."

Sam nodded absently. "Liana has some terrible event in her past that she's hiding from me, because she thinks I'll hate her." He let out a harsh laugh. "I couldn't hate her if I wanted to, but I can't convince her of that if I can't see her, and she says she wants to call it quits."

His grandfather leaned back in his chair and stroked his chin. "So what are you going to do?"

Sam turned his back on his grandfather and stared out the window at the mountains. That's what he'd been asking himself over and over again. What he needed was a plan to rattle Liana's cage, and he had to come up with one quickly, because he was running out of time.

But what kind of plan could he devise that would let him discover whether she loved him, and if she did, to get her to admit it? Somehow Sam knew if he could get her to say the words, then everything would work out. He knew it would. He just knew it, and as he continued to stare at the mountains, his plan came together.

"I'm going to take her into the mountains," he declared as he turned back around and grinned at his grandfather.

"Sounds like a good plan to me," the old man said with a chuckle.

"Yeah. Thanks, Gramps." He gave his grandfather's shoulder a squeeze. "I don't know what I'd do without you."

"All I've really done is listen, Sam, and you don't need me for that." He tapped his finger against his chest. "Everything you need to know is right in here. Follow your heart, and ninety-nine times out of a hundred you'll make the right choices."

Sam shivered, even though the room was toasty warm. He knew what his grandfather was trying to tell him, but he refused to acknowledge it. People who loved you as deeply as his grandfather loved him didn't leave when you still needed them. As long as he believed that, then the old man would be around, especially now that he'd always have his mountains at his beck and call, Sam thought as his gaze moved over Liana's pictures his grandfather had had framed. There were so many of them that they nearly filled an entire wall.

"You're probably right, but I'll still be dropping by for a second opinion," he said as he walked to the door. "Tell Mom I'm sorry I missed her, but I'll be back in a day or two."

"I'll tell her, and good luck with your Liana, Sam."

"Yeah. I have a feeling I'm going to need all the luck I can get."

His grandfather gave him a thumb's up sign, and Sam returned it, but when he walked out the front door, he shivered again.

"It's just the cold," he told himself. "It's just the damn cold."

So why did it feel like a premonition?

LIANA HADN'T HEARD A WORD from Sam in four days, and his silence was killing her. She knew she'd told him to call when he was ready to go into the mountains, but she was worried about him. He'd been so angry and so hurt when she'd told him she couldn't continue seeing him, and for at least the hundredth time she reached for the phone beside her bed to call him. But even as she started to dial his number, she knew she couldn't call. If she did, she'd be encouraging him, and that was too cruel.

She hung up and got off the bed. She had to go for a walk. If she didn't work off some of this excess tension, she was going to go nuts.

"Adriane, I'm going for a walk!" she yelled over the noise of the television set as she headed for the front door.

"Okay!" the girl yelled back.

Liana pulled on her coat, threw open her front door and let out a frightened yelp when she found Sam standing there. He took a quick step back, seemingly as startled by her sudden appearance as she was by him.

"Sorry. I didn't mean to scare you," Sam said, giving her a contrite smile. "I was just getting ready to ring the doorbell."

Liana pressed her hand against her racing heart, unable to determine whether it had decided to try out for the Indianapolis 500 because of fright or because of the luscious sight of Sam dressed in tight denims and a baggy navy-blue sweatshirt with the sleeves pushed up to his elbows. He would probably look gorgeous in ruffles and lace, she thought in vexation, as her body automatically responded.

Play it cool, she told herself, as she stared at his beloved face and watched a playful breeze toss his hair around while she fought against the impulse to throw herself into his arms. *Just play it cool.*

"Come on in, Sam," she said.

He shook his head. "I've got an appointment, and I'm already running late. I just wanted to let you know that I've landed a big roofing contract that will start in two weeks. I'd like to get my grandfather's pictures out of the way as soon as possible, and there's only one area left that I really want photographed for him.

"It's the four-day trip into the high country," he explained. "I checked with the Forest Service today. They say the area's open and the weather prediction is for blue skies and sunny weather. I know it's short notice, but could you leave the day after tomorrow?"

The significance of what he was saying caused a lump to form in Liana's throat. Sam was telling her that he'd be walking out of her life in another five or six days, and she'd been planning on having another couple of weeks. She wasn't prepared for the end to come this soon.

But what could she say? No was definitely out of the question. But yes would be so final. She knew she was arguing semantics, but she compromised with, "The day after tomorrow will be fine, Sam."

Sam couldn't help but feel disappointed by her answer, even though he hadn't expected a different one. In fact that's exactly why he'd decided to cut their time short. He was hoping that when it hit Liana that in a few days she'd never see him again she'd be forced into dealing with her feelings for him, and Sam was convinced that she cared about him. It might not be love yet, but she cared, and it was a step in the right direction.

But she was standing there looking as unmoved and unruffled as the first day he'd arrived on her doorstep, and it hurt. Really hurt. However, Sam forced himself to look at the situation pragmatically. He'd fallen in love with her, but, thankfully, he hadn't confessed his love to her, so if it didn't work out, he was going to be all right. It was a small distinction, but a significant one nonetheless, because as he'd determined before, one involved offering his heart and the other involved getting it cast aside. He knew he couldn't handle that kind of rejection from her.

"Good," he said as formally as he could and hoped she hadn't heard the slight quaver in his voice. "I have all the equipment we'll need for the trip, and I'll supply the food. If Adriane can't take care of Hooligan, my mother said she'd be happy to look after him. Just call my office and leave a message if I need to make arrangements for him."

"That's very kind of your mother," she said. "But I'm sure Adriane can handle him. Is there anything else?"

Yes. I love you. I miss you. I want to spend the rest of my life with you, he answered inwardly. Aloud, he said, "No, that's it. I'll see you the day after tomorrow."

With that, he turned and walked away, unaware that Liana was staring after him with tears in her eyes. She'd better get used to this scene, she told herself, for in just a few days it would happen again. When it did, it would mean that she'd never see him again and she had to be prepared for it.

But how in the world was she going to prepare herself? How was she going to find the courage to say goodbye?

She couldn't say goodbye, she suddenly realized, but how could she avoid it? There had to be a way that she could walk away without having to say goodbye. There had to be, because if there wasn't she wouldn't be able to bear the pain.

"YOU DON'T REALLY EXPECT ME to spend four days alone with that cat!" Adriane exclaimed in disbelief. "Come on, Liana. That's above and beyond the call of sisterly duty and you know it. Hooligan doesn't even like me."

"Of course he likes you," Liana argued. "He's just very reserved about it."

"He bit me the other day. That's not reserved. That's outright aggression."

"If you recall, he bit you because you stepped on his tail. If someone stepped on your tail, wouldn't you retaliate?"

"If I do this for you, you're going to owe me, Liana. And I mean owe me big. Just how do you intend on paying me back?"

Liana sat down on the sofa next to her sister and said, "If you do this for me, the minute I come back we'll catch the first plane to New York and I'll tell Mom and Dad to let you join the Marine Corps."

Adriane eyed her suspiciously. "This is that important to you?"

Liana nodded, because there was no way she was going to leave Hooligan with Sam's mother. She'd decided that the only way she could leave him without having to say good-bye was to drive her own car up to the mountains rather than riding with him. At the end of the trip she'd find a way to sneak away from him and get back to her car alone. Then she'd drive away from him and never look back, but there was no way she could carry out her plan if she had to pick up Hooligan.

She also knew that she wasn't really bribing her sister, because she'd already decided that it was time she came face-to-face with her parents. Having Adriane here had shown her how desperately she missed her family, and she had to mend the fences. Her parents might not be able to forgive her for what she'd done, but she did know that they still loved her. If they didn't, her mother wouldn't have continued to write. She wanted to be a part of their lives again, and she wanted to meet her new nephew. Maybe he could fill the gap that would be left by Sam, she thought with a wistful sigh.

"All right," Adriane agreed, albeit grudgingly. "I'll take care of the cat."

"Thank you," Liana said in a rush of relief. Now her only problem was getting herself mentally prepared for four platonic days in the mountains with Sam at her side. It was going to be hard, but she'd do it. She had to, because she didn't have a choice.

SAM FELT LIKE SANTA CLAUS. He'd checked his list once. He'd checked his list twice. And now he was checking it thrice.

He knew he had all the equipment and food that he and Liana could possibly need for far more than four days in the mountains, but the exercise kept his mind occupied, and he needed that.

Tomorrow would be the beginning of his last crusade with Liana. By the end of the trip he'd know for certain what her feelings were for him. If she loved him, then she'd have to beat him off with a stick, secret past or not, and he'd spend the rest of his life convincing her that nothing she ever did could make him hate her. Absolutely nothing. And if she didn't love him? He'd handle it. It would be hard, but he'd handle it.

He finally tossed the list aside. He was having dinner with his mother and Tom tonight. It was to be a celebratory dinner for his mother's engagement, and even though there was still a part of him that was torn over the event, Sam truly wanted her to be happy. He just wished Liana could be there with him. It would be a lot easier to handle if she was, because, as she'd said, he was being asked to impose Tom's image over his father's. Now that he'd found a measure of peace with his father's death, it was going to be hard as hell to do that.

However, Liana wouldn't be there, so he'd deal with it in the best way he knew how. With a stiff upper lip and a smile on his face, and what the heck, it was a lot better than sitting around here all night brooding about Liana.

"WHAT DO YOU MEAN you want to drive your own car?" Sam asked angrily as he stood in Liana's kitchen while she finished packing some freeze-dried food into her backpack.

"Just that," Liana said.

"Liana, it's ridiculous to take two cars."

She gave him a bright, if forced smile. "So, I'm ridiculous. I'm ready to leave. How about you?"

What Sam was ready to do was throttle her. If he couldn't reach her in the moutains, he only had four days left with her. Four very short days and he didn't want to miss one minute of them. Since it was a three-hour drive to their destination and a three-hour drive back, he'd be losing six hours of those days if she followed him in her car. Three-hundred-and-sixty long minutes that he didn't want to lose, and, by damn, he wasn't going to lose them.

"We're taking my car, and only my car."

Liana arched a brow as she grabbed her purse off the floor and slung it over her shoulder. "Machismo doesn't suit you, Sam. You're too nice a guy."

"Well, I'm not feeling very nice right now."

She gave him another bright smile. "You'll get over it."

"The hell I will."

"Come on, Sam. We're wasting time," she said as she walked out of the kitchen.

With a curse, he followed her, pausing to make sure her front door was locked since Adriane was still in bed. By the time he'd done that, she was already in her car with the motor running, and outside of slashing her tires, he knew he was beat.

"Damn woman," he muttered, finally accepting defeat and climbing into his four-wheel drive. "Damn woman," he repeated when they pulled onto the Interstate and he had to slow down so she could keep up with him.

He'd get even with her for this, he decided. He swore he'd get even with her if it was the last thing he ever did.

WHEN THEY ARRIVED at their destination and Sam refused to talk to her outside of a few curt directions, Liana knew he was still angry, so she didn't object when he took the lead as they hiked into the wilderness. She wasn't, however, particularly pleased about being forced to stare at his backside. She kept telling herself that her breathlessness was due to the altitude and the fact that she was carrying more weight than usual. But half an hour later, she was tired of trying to fool herself. Sam was a sexy devil and she wanted him. Since there was no way she could indulge herself in that pleasure, she was going to have to find something else to occupy her thoughts.

She began to survey her surroundings, searching for something to photograph. Unfortunately, there were only towering evergreens and aspens lining the sides of the trail, and not one of them had the good grace to be twisted into an interesting configuration that would warrant wasting her film. With a resigned sigh, she returned her attention to Sam and decided that she wanted memories of him, so she might as well start making them.

Sam knew he was behaving childishly by giving Liana the silent treatment, but he couldn't help himself. He loved her, dammit, and the fact that she might not return his feelings was hard enough to deal with. To have her steal away part of the few remaining hours he had left with her just wasn't fair.

But what else was new? he wondered angrily. Very few things in his life had been fair. It was as if he was cursed to always have a taste of the best life had to offer, only to have it snatched away before he could have his fill, and he couldn't figure out why.

Sure he had his faults, but he wasn't any worse than the next man, and better than a lot of them he'd seen. He worked hard at being honest and decent, and he never purposely hurt anyone. Because he had a short temper, he sometimes inadvertently stepped on someone's feelings, but when he did, he was always quick to apologize and then went out of his way to make it up to them. So why was it that he always received a kick in the butt instead of being rewarded for his efforts?

It just wasn't fair, he reiterated to himself, deciding that it was okay to indulge in a little self-pity when self-pity was in order.

By the time lunch rolled around and Sam still wasn't talking, Liana knew she was going to have to do something to ease the tension. She didn't want the last of their time together to be this way.

She waited until they were eating before she said, "I'm sorry you're angry with me, Sam, but can't we make peace? I want us to enjoy the next few days and part as friends."

"Friends?" he repeated disparagingly. "After what we've shared together, you want us to be friends?"

"Yes. Is that so hard to believe?"

"Yes, it is, because when I look at you, I don't see a friend. I see a woman who comes to life in my arms. I see lips that melt against mine. I see arms and legs that wrap around me and cling to me when I'm bringing you to fulfillment. That isn't a friend. That's a lover."

"But lovers are supposed to be friends, too," she said as she gazed at him miserably.

"The key word there is 'too,' and I can't be friends with a lover who will walk away from what we have for no sensible reason."

Liana shook her head, knowing what he was saying and understanding every word of it. But how could she make him see her side of this? How could she make him understand without telling him the whole sordid story? Maybe she should tell him the whole story, she thought, but she knew she was too ashamed to do it.

"If you won't give me friendship, will you at least give me civility for the remainder of the trip?"

Sam closed his eyes, telling himself that they'd just fought round one, and even if he had lost it, the fight wasn't over.

"Yes, Liana, I'll give you civility."

"Thank you."

"You're welcome."

And Sam worked hard at being civil. In fact he tried to drown her in civility, because he knew over-politeness could be as maddening as rudeness. The way he saw it, it would start to drive her up a wall and she'd get angry if nothing else. He wouldn't mind having a good fight, because people often revealed their true feelings during an argument.

Unfortunately, Liana didn't comply by getting angry. In fact, if anything she became more cheerful, and Sam decided that he hated cheerful. He despised cheerful. He'd like to throw rocks at cheerful.

Liana couldn't decide which was worse. Sam's silence or his butter-wouldn't-melt-in-my-mouth politeness. It was going to drive her crazy. Absolutely nuts. But she'd asked for civility and he'd given it to her, so she couldn't possibly complain. All she could do was plaster on a smile and act like a happy camper.

By the time they made camp and ate dinner, Sam was in such a foul mood that he would have snapped at a chipmunk. The worst part was, what did two supposedly civil people say to each other when there was nothing to do but sit and stare at the fire? The weather, he supposed, and since he'd listened to a few forecasts for just about every part of the world on the drive up here, he should be able to kill an hour or two. Now, how cold was it supposed to be in Alaska tonight?

Liana decided that she would give her eyeteeth for Adriane's television set right now, because she felt as if she were stuck in a time warp with a meterologist. If Sam made one more comment about the weather, she was going to bite his head off. She finally decided to call it a night, even if she was wide awake. She pulled the pins out of her hair to release her braid, and then began to unravel it.

Sam's breath caught in his throat, and he almost choked on it as Liana loosened her braid and pulled her hair free. He thought he could handle her stripping naked and dancing around the campfire more than he could handle watching her free her hair, because he was so darn fascinated with it. When she started to brush it, he came to his feet like a shot. He knew that if he didn't get out of there he wasn't going to be able to keep his hands off her.

"I'm going for a walk," he told her tightly. "Don't wait up, and don't worry about the fire. I'll take care of it when I get back."

Liana watched him walk into the darkness, wondering if she should ask him if he had a flashlight, however, he disappeared so quickly that she didn't have a chance. She told herself not to worry about him, because he knew what he was doing.

But after she got settled in her tent, she couldn't relax, and she knew she wouldn't until she heard him come back. It seemed like forever when she finally heard him, though she knew it couldn't have been more than twenty or thirty minutes.

She made herself lie down and close her eyes, but her ears were listening to his every movement. At first she thought he was getting ready for bed, but when the fire didn't go out, she knew she had to at least take a peek to see if everything was all right.

She pulled back the tent flap and her heart lurched. He was sitting in front of the fire, his shoulders slumped and his head cradled in his hands. He looked so vulnerable and so unhappy that tears flew into her eyes.

She couldn't go to him, she told herself. She was doing this for his own good. If she went to him now, it wouldn't be a clean break. But how could she stay away from him when it was so evident that he was hurting? With a resigned sigh, she slipped back into her clothes.

She knew he hadn't heard her approach when she touched his shoulder and he jumped in surprise. He glanced up at her and then quickly away, but he hadn't been fast enough to hide the misery in his eyes.

Liana knelt beside him and said, "What's the matter, Sam?"

"Nothing," he said gruffly, keeping his head averted. "I'm just not tired."

"I think you're still angry with me. Would it make you feel better if you yelled at me?"

"No," he said with a weary sigh. "Besides, if I start yelling, I might not be able to stop. I also think we should go home tomorrow."

That momentarily stunned Liana. "But you said this is your grandfather's favorite trail. Don't you want pictures of it for him?"

"Yes," he said as he finally looked at her. "But I can't be this close to you without touching you. It's killing me, Liana, and if I have to spend three more days like this, I know I'll die."

Liana might have been able to ignore his wretched expression, but she could never have ignored the wounded look in his eyes.

"Then touch me," she said, opening her arms.

Sam told himself he couldn't do it. He was already so much in love with her that he couldn't stand it, and if at the end of the trip she walked away from him, it would be even more painful if they'd made love.

But what could hurt worse than what he was feeling now? As long as he functioned on the precept that it was going to be over in three days, then he could protect himself. It didn't mean he'd give up hope. He just wouldn't build his hopes up, and he reached for her, because he couldn't have stopped himself from doing it if he'd wanted to.

When Sam crushed her to him, Liana knew that what she was doing was wrong. If he was in this pain now, how would he feel in three days when she left? Not only that, how would she feel? It would tear her apart, but her only other option was to compound his hurt by stealing away his grandfather's pictures, and she couldn't do that to him.

There was only one way to deal with the situation, she decided. Live the next three days to their fullest so that the beautiful memories would balance out the pain for both of them.

"Put out the fire, Sam," she murmured. "While you're doing that, I'll get my sleeping bag. Your tent's bigger than mine."

"Just get the sleeping bag," he whispered as he kissed her. "We don't need a tent."

Chapter Thirteen

"Mmm," Sam hummed lazily as he snuggled closer to Liana and basked in the softness of her skin next to his. "I don't think I'll ever be able to look at the moon or smell wood smoke without thinking of you lying in my arms."

Liana sifted his hair through her fingers, enchanted with the feel of it and the way it clung to her fingers. "Me, too."

"I suppose we ought to get into the tent."

"I suppose so."

"I don't want to move."

"So don't."

Sam levered himself up on his elbow and grinned at her. "The bears might get us."

"They'd be too embarrassed. In fact, we've horrified every forest creature within a hundred miles by frolicking in the open in front of a fire."

Sam chuckled. "We're also likely to horrify a few happy campers in the morning if we don't find some cover."

Liana gave some thought to that. Even though it wasn't the season for backpacking, the weather had been warm enough to encourage the more devout followers of the sport. The chances of her and Sam getting caught au naturel in a sleeping bag were pretty slim, but she wasn't a person to play the odds.

She released a reluctant sigh. "I suppose you're right. We'd better get into the tent."

But when she began to sit up, Sam caught her shoulder and held her in place. Liana frowned as she noted that his grin had disappeared, replaced by a worried expression.

"What's wrong?" she asked.

Sam cleared his throat and cursed the blush he could feel flooding his cheeks. "Nothing. It's that I just realized that I, uh... Oh, hell, Liana. I just realized that I didn't use anything to protect you. But don't worry about it. If anything happens, I'll do the right thing," he said in a rush.

"Oh, Sam," Liana said with an amused laugh. She reached up and caressed his cheek. "When God made you, he broke the mold. Haven't you ever heard the old saying that nice guys finish last?"

"A man is supposed to take responsibility for his actions," he responded stiffly.

"Yes, a man is," she agreed, realizing she'd offended him. "But so is a woman, Sam. As my mother would say, it takes two to tango, and I'd never trap a man into marriage over a pregnancy. Besides, this discussion is moot. It's a safe time of the month for me."

"You're sure," he stated, and wondered why he felt disappointed when she nodded. He wasn't the type of cad who would try to trap a woman into marriage. Or was he? When it came to Liana, he wasn't sure that he wouldn't resort to every trick in the book.

But he didn't want her through tricks. He wanted her because she loved him and wanted to be with him for the rest of her life, and as she smiled up at him with so much loving tenderness in her eyes, he began to believe that that might actually be possible.

"If we don't get into the tent in the next five seconds, I will not be held accountable for my actions," he told her huskily.

"So, who wants you to be accountable?"

THE NEXT THREE DAYS were filled with laughter and wonder for Liana. For each picture she took, Sam kissed her twice, and she began to find reasons to take pictures of the most mundane scenes.

But as they made love on their final night together, she realized this was the last time she'd hold him in her arms. The thought made her desperate, for even though she'd accepted the fact that this was all the time she would have with him, she still wanted more.

If only Sam had come into her life years ago, maybe things would have been different. She'd loved Bill deeply, but what she felt for Sam was so much more intense. There was a vulnerability to Sam that Bill had never had. There was also an innate kindness to Sam that tugged at her heartstrings. He'd given her the most wonderful memories to carry with her for the remainder of her life, and she prayed that she'd given him the same in return.

"I love you," Sam told her after they'd made love, unable to hold the words back any longer. They were no more than an hour's hike away from the car, and he was getting desperate. He knew Liana loved him. He could see it in her eyes. Hear it in her voice. Feel it in her touch. Taste it on her lips. Smell it on her skin. So why hadn't she said so?

He'd told himself that he wouldn't build his hopes up, but he had. These last few days together had been the most wonderful days of his life, and he wanted them to go on forever. If she'd just say the words, he knew that dream would come true.

Tears welled into Liana's eyes and she shook her head. "No, Sam, you don't love me. You love the woman you think I am. But I'm not that woman, and if you knew the truth about me, you'd hate me."

"I keep telling you that I could never hate you, Liana, and I'll prove it to you," he told her solemnly.

She gave him an indulgent smile as she brushed his hair off his forehead. "How are you going to do that?"

"You're going to tell me what you've done, and then you're going to find out that my feelings for you haven't changed."

For a very brief moment, Liana was tempted to do what he suggested. It would be a relief to bare her soul to him, to tell him about South America, about Bill, and maybe, just maybe, he was right. Maybe he wouldn't hate her. Maybe they could build a future together.

But as she gazed up into his expressive eyes she remembered the horror and disgust she's seen in her parents' eyes, and she knew she couldn't take the chance that Sam would respond the same way. If she took that one last step and he turned away from her, she'd never get over it. Never.

"We'll talk about it tomorrow," she whispered as she drew his head down to hers and gave him a kiss, knowing in her heart that tomorrow would never come. By the time he woke up, she'd be gone. She had to be gone, because now more than ever, she knew she couldn't bear to tell him goodbye. "Just love me for now, Sam. Make love to me, and let me love you back."

Sam, sensing something akin to hopelessness in her plea, rebelled at first, but as her lips begged him to return her kisses and her body moved sinuously against his, he finally gave in. He'd make love to her tonight, but tomorrow he was going to get some answers. He wanted to marry Liana. He wanted to build a life with her. He wanted it all, and he knew they could have it if she'd only trust him. She had to trust him, he thought, growing even more desperate as she took control of their lovemaking and drove him to madness.

"I love you!" he exclaimed urgently as they finally joined and rushed toward fulfillment.

"And I love you!" she exclaimed urgently when they reached a shattering climax, knowing she had to give him at least that much.

Sam's heart soared, because she'd finally said the words. He wasn't going to lose her now, and he knew it. All his dreams for the future were going to come true.

"I love you," he whispered again as he hugged her to him in ecstasy.

"And I love you," Liana whispered back, hugging him in farewell.

"Promise me that we'll talk tomorrow," he said.

"I promise," Liana said, crossing her fingers behind his back.

It was those two words that kept Sam from fighting against sleep. Tomorrow they'd work it out. She'd said she loved him, and that was all that mattered. As long as she loved him, they could work it out.

SAM KNEW LIANA WAS GONE before he opened his eyes, but he didn't want to believe it. He refused to believe it.

As he climbed out of the sleeping bag and dressed, he kept telling himself that she was out taking pictures. So, her backpack was gone. She needed it for extra film, right? There was no other explanation, because she couldn't tell him she loved him in one breath and then walk out on him with the next. She wouldn't promise him tomorrow and then walk away without telling him why. She couldn't leave him without saying goodbye.

All he had to do was start breakfast and then she'd come back. She'd tell him about the photographs she'd taken while she sipped her tea. They'd share a kiss or two. A hug or two. He'd murmur something suggestive, and she'd murmur something suggestive back. Then they'd share another kiss, he'd haul her back into the tent and they'd make love, where she'd tell him again that she loved him.

She wouldn't promise me tomorrow and then leave without telling me why. She wouldn't leave without telling me goodbye.

But she had, and he knew it. Why was it so easy for the people he loved to leave him without an explanation? Didn't they know how much that hurt? Wasn't he worth at least a note, even if it was one damning him to hell? It was evident that they didn't think he was worth it, but why?

Sam hadn't cried since he was ten years old, but as he stared at the pile of wood he'd gathered for a fire, tears began to roll down his cheeks. He shed twenty years' worth of anguished tears over his father. He shed two years' worth of anguished tears over Kay. But when it came to Liana, he didn't just cry. He sobbed. Her desertion hurt the most, because he'd told her about his father and his ex-wife. He'd told her how much it had hurt when they'd abandoned him. He'd told her, but it hadn't made a difference.

When he had finally released his grief, he felt empty, and for one brief—one very fleeting—second, he wondered if his father hadn't found the perfect solution to life's agonies.

But even as he formulated that thought, he knew he couldn't kill himself. He might put himself out of his misery if he did, but he'd end up inflicting misery on his mother, his grandfather, his employees and their families. There were too many people who depended on him to be there for them, and he simply couldn't do it. His mother had been right about that, he realized, and he'd never doubt a mother's heart for as long as he lived.

As he took down the tent, his mind began to stray to thoughts of Liana, but Sam reeled it back in. From this moment on, Liana Stevens didn't exist and never had. And to make sure of it the minute he got home he'd take her photographs of endangered species off his wall and throw them into the trash. Then he'd go see his grandfather. If anyone could help him deal with the pain, it would be his grandfather.

"COME ON, LIANA, what are you waiting for?" Adriane asked as she hauled Hooligan's pet carrier out of the cab. "You were so anxious to get here that you called me long distance at some ungodly hour to tell me to be waiting at the door and ready to leave when you got home. Now that we're here, you're dragging your feet. The meter's running, and you're costing us a fortune, so get out of the cab."

"In a minute," Liana murmured as she stared at her parents' house. It was so familiar, and yet it looked so foreign. The words, *You can never come home again,* kept flashing through her mind. But she was home, wasn't she? This was home. It always had been and it always would be, so why did it feel so strange.

Because in her heart, home would always be with Sam. Sam. Beautiful, wonderful Sam. It had been so hard to walk away, but she'd had to do it, hadn't she? Of course, she had, but . . .

She couldn't think of buts. It was over, and now she had to move on. She climbed out of the cab.

The front door opened as she and Adriane mounted the steps, and Liana's heart stopped as she watched her father wheel her mother out in a wheelchair. She had been right.

There'd been something wrong. Something terribly wrong! Oh, God, why hadn't she called? Why had she stayed away?

"Mom?" she said hesitantly when she finally stood only a few steps away.

"Come here, baby," her mother said as she opened her arms, and Liana began to cry, because there wasn't one ounce of horror, disgust or hatred in her mother's eyes. There was only love and tears of happiness.

"I told you those acting lessons would pay off," Adriane said, her own voice choked with tears as she went to their father. "I also told you I'd get her home. I promised you I'd do it, and I did."

SAM KNEW HE LOOKED LIKE HELL, but if a shower and a shave couldn't fix him up, nothing would. He also knew that he couldn't stay away from his grandfather. He had to see the old man. He had to talk to him. He had to have his re-assurance that everything was going to be all right, because once he had it, he knew it would be true.

But when he walked into his mother's house, he only had to take one look at her face to know that he'd never get his grandfather's reassurance again.

He shook his head, because even though he knew in his heart that the old man was gone, he refused to believe it. His grandfather wouldn't leave him without saying goodbye. He loved him too much to leave him like that, and he ran toward the old man's bedroom, knowing he'd be there. He had to be there. He wouldn't do this to him. He wouldn't.

But when he threw open the door the room was empty. Sam shook his head again, still refusing to believe. *He wouldn't leave without saying goodbye!*

"Sam?" his mother questioned worriedly as she touched his arm.

Sam pulled away from her and headed for the front door. "I know where he's at," he said frantically. "He'll be waiting for me so we can say goodbye. He will."

"IT'S TIME WE TALKED," Liana murmured as she accepted the tea cup her mother handed her, still finding it difficult to see her in a wheelchair and heartsick that she hadn't been there for her.

Her mother had been in a car accident four months before and had suffered a spinal injury. She'd had extensive surgery and would need even more. It would be many more months before they'd know if she'd ever recover the use of her legs.

"Why didn't you tell me about the accident?" she asked mournfully. "I would have come, Mama. You know I would've come."

"Yes, we knew you'd come," her father stated as he sat down beside her. "But since your mother wasn't critical, we decided not to tell you. We wanted you to come home on your own, because we knew if you didn't, you wouldn't stay."

"That isn't true," she objected fervently. "I would have stayed until I knew everything was all right."

"Yes," her mother agreed. "But then you would have run away again, Liana, and we couldn't stand the thought of reliving that hell. We wanted to help you so badly when you came back from South America, but before we could even assimilate what you'd told us, you'd taken off. Why didn't you stay and talk it out so we could help you?"

Tears welled into Liana's eyes. "I couldn't let you help me. I saw that look of horror and disgust in your eyes, and I knew you hated me. I just couldn't bear to see it again."

"Oh, Liana, no!" her mother exclaimed as she grabbed her hand and gave it a squeeze. "What you saw in our eyes might have been horror, but it was horror out of pure terror. We'd just learned that you'd nearly been killed. As far as hating you, you know better than that. Your father and I could never hate you. You're our daughter, and we love you."

"But don't you see that that's just it?" she stated plaintively. "You knew what I did to Bill, and you loved me anyway. I don't deserve your love, and you both know it."

"What in the world are you talking about?" her father demanded impatiently. "You keep referring to what you did to Bill, but what about what he did to you? My word, child, the man claimed he loved you, yet he knowingly put your life in jeopardy!"

"No, he didn't. You don't know what went on that day, and there are so many details I can't tell you, so there's no way I can make you understand."

"Liana, you're wrong," her father said. "Your mother and I do understand, and what we understand is that Bill endangered your life to try to get himself a big promotion. He used you."

"He didn't use me!" she shouted angrily. "And how can you sit there and pick on him when he can't defend himself?"

"Because it's the truth!" her mother exclaimed just as angrily. "I'm sorry, Liana. I know you loved Bill, but what he did to you was selfish and self-centered. Not once did he consider your safety. If he had, he would have never taken you with him."

"No," Liana said, shaking her head adamantly against their claim. "You're not right. He needed me and my camera to verify his story, and he did consider my safety. If he hadn't I wouldn't be alive. He did look out for me, but I didn't look out for him."

She rose to her feet and began to prowl the room. "It just happened so fast. It was like it was over before it began, but if I'd just done something, I know he'd be alive today."

"Liana, you just said that it happened so fast it was over before it began," her mother said with feeling. "Think about that. You were frightened, and you had a delayed reaction. That's exactly how I had my accident. I saw that car run the red light and I was so momentarily frightened that I couldn't hit the brakes. By the time I tried to, it was too late."

"It's not the same thing," Liana said as she stopped pacing and hugged her arms around her middle. "When you love someone enough to marry them, you are supposed to love them enough to risk your life for them. Because I couldn't, Bill is dead."

Her father came to her and pulled her into his arms. As he held her, he said, "Even if what you're saying is true, Liana, what about the other side of the coin? A man who loves you is supposed to love you enough to keep you from harm. Do you honestly think that I would ever purposely put your mother in a potentially dangerous situation?"

"He's right, Liana," Adriane stated from the doorway. "And if you'd gone to that counselor the government referred you to instead of going into hiding, you wouldn't be sitting here in such a mess today. Stop running away and start listening for once."

Liana glanced toward her sister in dread. "How long have you been standing there? I didn't want you to know about this."

"Good heavens, Mom and Dad told me everthing a few weeks after you took off," Adriane muttered. "They weren't the only ones hurting. My big sister promised to be at my high school graduation, and then a month beforehand, she takes off for parts unknown. How do you think I felt about that?''

"Oh, I'm so sorry," Liana said as she flew across the room and hugged Adriane. "I was so distraught that I didn't even remember your graduation."

"I know," Adriane assured as she hugged her back. "When Mom and Dad told me what had happened, I understood. But it's time to put the past behind you, Liana. And think about what Dad said, will you? You say you had a responsibility, but Bill had a responsibility, too. Would Sam haul you into a situation where you might be killed?''

"We're talking about two different people," Liana noted as she pulled away from Adriane, feeling as if she were being bombarded from all directions. They were getting her so darn confused! She had been wrong, and she knew it. So why were they all talking as if she had been an innocent victim?

"Yes, we are talking about two different people," Adriane stated staunchly. "Sam is a man who'd protect you with his life. Bill was a man who'd risk your life for a stupid job. I may be nearly thirteen years younger than you, Liana, but I'm smart enough to understand that much, so would you please stop playing martyr and grow up? I'm supposed to be the baby around here."

Before Liana could respond, the girl shoved an envelope into her hands. "Here are the pictures you asked me to have developed at that one-hour place. I still think you ought to hop on the next plane and give them to Sam personally, but at least send a note along with them when you drop them in the mail. Maybe you can salvage some of those bridges you set on fire when you hightailed it out of Denver."

"Who's Sam?" her mother inquired curiously.

"Just the greatest thing to come along since the Lone Ranger," Adriane answered. She tossed her head in Liana's direction. "Unfortunately, he was stupid enough to fall in love with the cowardly lion over there."

Liana paled as Adriane's words sent her flipping back in time, and she saw Sam sitting on a ledge and grinning down at her as he said, "You can stop being a cowardly lion and open your eyes now."

"Liana? Are you all right?" her father said in concern.

She looked up at him and had to shake her head, because for one brief second, she was staring up at Sam. How many times had he asked her that question with that same loving concern in his voice? More times than she cared to remember.

And what was it her mother had said a few minutes ago? *Your father and I could never hate you.* Sam had said, *I could never hate you, and I'll prove it to you. You're going to tell me what you've done, and then you're going to find out that my feelings haven't changed.*

And at that moment Liana knew that she loved him so completely and so passionately that she would lay down her life for him without a second thought. So why had it been so different with Bill?

"Oh, my God, what have I done?" she whispered when it all fell into place. "I just lost three years of my life with all of you because I thought you hated me when you didn't. I should have given Sam a chance. I should have told him everything and given him a chance. Because I didn't, I may have lost him forever!"

"By George, I think she's finally got it!" Adriane said with a squeal. "Want me to make you a plane reservation? I figured you'd eventually come to your senses, so I've already checked the airline schedule. There's a plane leaving for Denver in about two hours. You can be there before midnight."

"But she just got here!" her mother objected.

"Oh, she'll be back, and wait until you see what she brings back with her," Adriane chortled.

"Adriane's right, Mama," Liana said as she rushed to her and gave her a hug. "Sam is the most wonderful man in the world, and you're going to love him. I promise you, you're going to love him to pieces. Just keep your fingers crossed that he's going to forgive me for treating him so badly, because if he doesn't . . . No, I'm not even going to think that way. I'm going to think positively. I have to think positively. Is it okay if I leave Hooligan here with you?"

"Oh, no!" Adriane exclaimed. "I just spent four days alone with that epitome of ugliness, and I refuse to have him underfoot any longer."

"Hey, you owe me. You lied to me about wanting to join the Marine Corps," Liana accused.

"No, I didn't," Adriane denied. "I lied about the fact that Mom and Dad wouldn't let me join. I'm leaving for boot camp in six weeks, and I wanted to make sure they had someone dependable around to keep an eye on them."

"I object to that," Liana's brother Sandy said as he walked into the room and plopped Liana's new nephew into her arms. "There isn't anyone more dependable than me."

"That's the trouble," his wife grumbled as she trailed in after him. "You're so dependable that you get underfoot."

Liana laughed as they each gave her a quick hug and then she turned her attention on the baby. "Oh, he's absolutely adorable!"

Sandy grinned. "Well, since you think he's so adorable, how are you at changing diapers?"

"I've had less experience than you," she answered as she passed the baby back to him. "And right now he needs changing."

"Aw, come on, Liana," he cajoled. "It'll be a piece of cake."

Liana smiled sweetly. "I've already broken one arm for that line. I don't do diapers, and even if I did, I have a plane to catch. With any luck I can start working on my own baby to change."

"What's she talking about?" Sandy asked in confusion when Liana rushed out the door.

"Good heavens, Sandy," Adriane said. "If you can't figure that one out, where in the world did you get Junior? From a cabbage patch?"

Liana didn't hear Sandy's response, but she was sure Adriane had pushed the right buttons to send him off on one of his lectures about the social graces of young women in mixed company.

When her plane began its descent at Stapleton Airport in Denver five hours later, Liana kept telling herself that it was going to be all right. Sam would forgive her. He loved her. He'd forgive her. So why did she have this terrible nagging feeling that he wouldn't?

Chapter Fourteen

He'll come soon, Sam told himself as he sat in vigil on the edge of the spring and watched nightfall creep across the valley. *He'll come, because this is his own secret little spot in heaven where the stream glows in the dark and the stars are so close that you can reach out and pluck them right out of the sky. He'll come, so we can say goodbye.*

When darkness finally fell, Sam waited patiently, not moving a muscle, barely breathing. He had to be still so he'd feel him when the old man came, because he'd be different now. But he'd know. He'd feel him in his heart. And it would be soon now. Very, very soon.

LIANA WAS FRANTIC. Sam wasn't at his apartment or his office. She knew he might be at his mother's, but she didn't know where the woman lived. In fact, she didn't even know her first name. He'd always referred to her as Mom or my mother.

It seemed so odd to Liana that they'd gone through such an emotional roller-coaster ride together that she knew Sam inside out, but she didn't know anything as mundane as his mother's name. Who could tell her where the woman lived?

It suddenly dawned on her that Neal had gone to school with Sam, so he might know. Heaven help her, he had to know, because she'd go insane with worry if she couldn't check the house. She pulled into a service station with a public phone.

Neal answered on the fifteenth ring with a curse and a muttered, "This better be one hell of an important call, because I'm in the middle of a close encounter of the intimate kind."

"Neal, I'm sorry, but it's Liana, and this is a matter of life and death. I have to find Sam, and he's not home. Do you know where his mother lives?"

"Where his mother lives?" he repeated, sounding dazed. "I used to know, but it's been so long that I can't really remember."

"Do you remember her name, then? Please, Neal, this is really important."

"Why's it so important?"

"Because it's urgent that I talk to him. Now, do you know his mother's name?"

"Oh, Lord, Liana, I don't know. It started with an A, I think."

Liana whipped open the phone book. There were only two women's names listed under the name Dillon in the A section.

"How about Abigail?" she asked, naming the first one.

"I think that's it! Yeah, I know it is, because I called her Abby once and Sam got mad as hell. If I remember right, his old man used to call her that, and she was really sensitive about it."

"Does the street Fairplay Way ring a bell?" she inquired, noting the address.

"I think that's it, too. How did you do that?"

"Phone book, silly. Look, I've gotta run, Neal, but I want you to start calling Sam's apartment for me. If you get hold of him and he hasn't seen me, tell him I'm sorry I left him. Tell him I'm looking for him. Tell him I have to talk to him. Tell him I'll keep coming back to his apartment until I find him. Thank you. You're the best friend ever. Bye."

"Liana, you can't hang up without telling me what this is all about!"

"I'll tell you later, Neal. I promise. Bye." She could hear him squawking when she hung up, but she didn't have time to explain what was going on. She had to find Sam.

She hurried into the service station, and luckily they had a city map. She found the street she was looking for, and she was sure it was Sam's mother, because it was only a couple of miles from his apartment building. As close as Sam was to his grandfather, he'd live nearby.

She made one more pass by his apartment on the way, but he still wasn't there. He had to be at his mother's. He just had to be, because she was worried sick about him.

However, the lights were off and there wasn't a car in sight. She was so upset she wanted to lay her head on the steering wheel and sob her eyes out. Where was he? She had to find him. She had to tell him she was sorry. She had to tell him about her past, and then she'd tell him how much she loved him. Where was he?

She'd go back to his apartment, she decided. He had to come home eventually, and when he did, she'd be waiting.

But Sam didn't come home, and after two hours crept by, Liana couldn't sit still any longer. She got out of her car, went to his door and started pacing in front of it.

She hadn't been pacing long when she saw a man approaching. At first she thought it was Sam because of his height, but as he moved closer she realized he was far too slender, and she was flodded with disappointment.

But her disappointment turned to fear when the man walked beneath the glow of a streetlight and she realized it was Neal. His face was set in such a grim line that Liana clutched at her stomach and she had to swallow hard against the bile rising in her throat. Something had happened to Sam!

"Neal, where's Sam?" she asked as she ran to meet him. "Where is he?"

"No one knows," he said as he ran his hand through his hair. "After your crazy call, I got worried, so I started calling his mother's house. I got hold of her awhile ago, and it seems Sam's grandfather died while you two were up in the mountains. When he found out this morning, he took off and hasn't been seen since."

"Oh, no!" Liana gasped in horror. It was bad enough that she'd left him, but then for him to come back and learn that his grandfather had died? She didn't even want to think about the repercussions, and if her stomach had been aching a minute ago, it was now ulcerating.

Where would he go? she asked herself as she searched her mind in a frenzy. Where would he go when he was in so much pain?

Think! she screamed at herself when all she got was a blank response. *You love this man. You may not know the mundane details of his life, but you know him inside out. Where would he go?*

All she could think of was the mountains, but where in the mountains? And suddenly, she knew exactly where he was.

"I know where he's at," she said as she began running toward her car.

"Liana, wait! I'll go with you," Neal yelled after her, but Liana didn't slow down. She had to do this alone. No one else could help Sam through this like she could, because no one loved his as much as she did.

"Be there, Sam," she whispered urgently as she turned onto the Interstate. "Please, be there and be safe."

SAM FOUGHT AGAINST THE PAIN as dawn approached and his grandfather hadn't come. He'd been so certain he'd come. If it was only for one brief second, he'd come. But he hadn't, and as the sun began to peek over the horizon, everything inside Sam folded up and died.

LIANA'S FOOT SLIPPED and she cursed softly as she clung to the side of the cliff. It seemed as if she'd been climbing for hours, and she'd hardly made any progress at all.

She knew Sam was up in the tunnel. Not only was his car parked at the foot of the trail, but this place was his grandfather's own little secret spot in heaven. This is where Sam would come to grieve for him.

She cursed again, when she started sliding backwards. It was bad enough that she'd had to wait until dawn to traverse the treacherous trail, but now she couldn't even get up the darn cliff, and she had to get to Sam. She had to get to him now. He'd already spent too much time alone. But for every foot she ascended, she seemed to slide back two.

"I can do this," she gritted from between her teeth as she tried again. "I can do it. I can. It worked for *The Little Choo-choo,* so it will work for me, too. I can do it. I can do it."

And she did do it, even if she did have a few more setbacks along the way. By the time she reached the ledge, she was nearly exhausted, and even though she wanted to rush right to the tunnel, she forced herself to sit until her arm and leg muscles stopped trembling.

Finally, she felt capable of standing, and she eased her way to her feet. She experienced a moment of vertigo, but it passed quickly, and she carefully made her way along the ledge. The moment she rounded the corner and stepped onto the plateau, she took off on a dead run and didn't stop until she entered the tunnel.

Sam was there all right. He was sitting at the edge of the spring and staring out over the valley as if he were some posted sentinel.

"Sam?" she said as she walked toward him. She experienced a fluttering of terrible fear when he didn't even twitch a muscle in response to her voice, because she suddenly knew that he wasn't going to forgive her. She'd run away to keep him from hating her, and by doing so, she'd made him hate her. The irony tasted bitter in her mouth.

SAM FROZE AT THE SOUND of Liana's voice, the pain started to rise but he forced it back into oblivion. He didn't want to feel. It hurt too much too feel. He wasn't going to feel.

"Sam?" Liana said again when she knelt down beside him. "Sam, I know you don't want to talk to me, but will you at least look at me? Please, Sam," she pleaded when he ignored her. "I have some things I have to tell you, and I need you to look at me."

She's not here, Sam told himself. *She's not here, because she doesn't exist. She's never existed. Ignore her, and she'll go away. No, that's wrong. She'd already gone away, so she didn't exist. Since she didn't exist, it was all right to look, wasn't it? Sure.*

Liana gasped and tears welled into her eyes when Sam finally pivoted his head toward her, because she realized how badly he hurt. His eyes were empty, and she understood that he'd become what she had been when he'd first walked into her life. A person whose pain was so intense that it was easier to turn off the light and pretend that the world didn't exist.

"Oh, Sam," she said on a sob and reached out to touch his cheek.

"Don't touch me," he stated in a low monotone as he jerked back from her touch. *She isn't supposed to be here,* he told himself. His grandfather was. Not her. Was that why the old man hadn't come? Had he stayed away because she'd come? That was it, and he knew it. It wasn't enough for her to walk away from him, but now she was keeping his grandfather away. He hated her. He *hated* her. But how could he hate her when she didn't exist?

Liana wanted to burst into tears when he continued to stare at her through those blank eyes, but she held them back. Tears weren't going to help. What she had to do was find a way to reach him. Even if she'd already lost him, she had to reach him. She loved him too much to let him suffer like this.

"I heard about your grandfather, and I am so sorry, Sam. I am so very, very sorry," she told him.

This time it was anger Sam felt, and he didn't know where to direct it, because he was so angry at so many people. But he was angry the most with her, he finally decided. She'd made him a promise, and then she'd gone away. No one else had made him any promises, but she had, and then she'd gone away. But it didn't matter, because she didn't exist, so he pushed the anger back.

"I don't want your condolences," he told her. "And I don't want you here."

It was that terrible monotone in his voice that hurt Liana the most. Sam was a man with so much feeling inside, and to hear him speaking so unemotionally was tearing her apart.

"I know you don't want me here," she replied, "and I'll go, Sam, but before I do, I want to explain why I left you like I did. I know it wasn't right for me to sneak away, but I love you so much that I didn't know how to say goodbye. I was so worried about protecting my own feelings that I didn't think of yours. That was very selfish of me, Sam, and if you hate me for it, I understand. I really do."

Sam blinked in surprise when the words, *I could never hate you,* flashed through his mind. But he did hate her. Hadn't he just decided that he hated her? No, he'd decided that she didn't exist.

"Just go away," he said, beginning to feel confused. He wanted her to go away because he didn't want to feel anything. Not even confusion. He just wanted to sit here and be left alone.

Liana felt her first spark of hope when he blinked at her words, and even though she knew it might be wishful thinking, she would swear that she could sense some subtle change in his posture. She hadn't quite figured out what it was yet, but something was changing.

"I will go, but before I do, I want to tell you my terrible secret. I kept hiding it from you because I was afraid you'd hate me, but since you most likely already hate me, what have I got to lose, right?"

Again, the words, *I could never hate you,* went through Sam's mind, and his confusion increased even further. He did hate her. She'd promised him tomorrow and then went away without saying goodbye. She went away without telling him why. He *had* to hate her. No, he didn't. Because she didn't exist. Why did he keep forgetting that?

"Do you want to hear my secret, Sam?" Liana asked when she finally figured out what the change was. He was breathing faster and deeper, as if he'd been walking fast, and she would swear she'd just seen something flicker in his eyes. It was weak, but it was there.

"Do you, Sam?" she prodded when he didn't answer.

"No," he told her, but it wasn't true. He wanted to know. He wanted to know, but why? She didn't exist any longer. He'd cast her out of his mind and his heart. It didn't matter any longer. So why did he want to know?

Liana sighed inwardly in relief when he suddenly raked his hand through his hair. Moving was a good sign, wasn't it? she asked herself. Up to this point he hadn't moved except to turn his head, so that had to be a good sign. She wished she could read his mind so she knew what was going on inside him, but since she couldn't, all she could do was keep talking.

"I'm going to tell you anyway, because I want you to know so you understand why I was so frightened to tell you."

But I don't want to know. It's too late! Sam railed inwardly. But somehow he couldn't bring himself to say the words aloud. He shivered suddenly when something seemed to move inside him, and he would have sworn he heard a voice whisper, "Listen."

"I'll listen," he said before he even realized it.

Liana sat down cross-legged and watched his face while she tried to pull her thoughts together. It had been so long since she'd actually told the story that she wasn't sure where she should begin.

Finally, she drew in a deep breath and said, "I was engaged to a news reporter named Bill Hawkins. His paper sent him to South America to cover the aftermath of an earthquake, and he asked me to go with him. While we were there, Bill got wind of a potential military coup in a neighboring country. He wanted to be a news reporter on national television news, but he hadn't even been able to get his foot in the door. He decided that if he got a scoop on the story, then he could write his own ticket."

She closed her eyes as the memories assailed her. The terror was no longer there, but the horror and the pain were. It took her a few moments before she could gain the strength to continue.

She opened her eyes and said, "Bill wanted me to go with him and take pictures to substantiate his story. I told him no, at first, but he kept badgering me. I was in love, and it's hard to say no to someone you love."

You said no to me, Sam thought, as the anger began to rise again. *You said you loved me and then you went away.* When the pain began to rise, he pushed both emotions away. She didn't exist. She didn't exist. She didn't!

"Anyway, we went to this town where everything was supposed to happen," Liana continued after a pause. "I was sure Bill was wrong, because there was such a carnival atmosphere there. It was as if everyone was having a great big party in the streets."

She had to close her eyes again, because the pain was growing in intensity. She felt the tears surface, but she held them back. She wasn't going to cry.

"Suddenly, the atmosphere began to change. It wasn't really anything I could put my finger on. I just knew something bad was going to happen. It was like I had a premonition."

Something inside Sam jerked at the word, and he remembered thinking it the day he'd left his grandfather after talking to him about Liana. He felt the pain coming again. Why hadn't he listened to that premonition? Why had he ignored it? If he'd listened to it, he could have been there to say goodbye.

Liana seemed to have read his thoughts, because she suddenly said, "I decided that I was being silly and I should ignore it, and I'll regret having made that decision for the rest of my life."

"Why?" Sam asked when she didn't continue. He was being drawn into the story despite himself, but he told himself it was all right. She didn't exist, so it was all right.

"The feeling came back, and I told Bill about it. He thought I was being silly, but he put me behind a rock wall and told me I'd be safe there. Then he told me to start taking pictures while he went out into the crowd to mingle."

Sam frowned when Liana suddenly stopped her story and drew her knees up to her chest. He could sense her distress and he felt a sudden urge to reach out and touch her, and he clenched his hands into fists. After what she'd done to him, he never wanted to touch her again, he told himself. Never. She didn't exist.

A long time passed before she finally said, "I saw a flash of something metallic in a window. At first it didn't register. I thought it was a shaft of sunlight hitting a pot or something. But then I saw more flashes. They were everywhere I looked. In the windows, on the roof, and I suddenly realized that there were men with guns surrounding us and no one knew it."

Tears filled her eyes and she drew in a shuddering breath. "I could see Bill across the street and I wanted to warn him, but I was so afraid that I couldn't even get out a squeak. The man I loved was in danger, and I kept telling myself to yell out to warn him, but I was frozen."

Sam felt another urge to touch her when her tears began to roll down her cheeks. He kept telling himself it was wrong, but he just couldn't seem to stop from laying his hand over hers. He'd give comfort to a wounded animal, so why not her? he offered himself as an excuse. Besides, if she didn't exist, it didn't matter.

Liana jumped at the contact and looked up at him, relieved to see that he was coming back. The light in his eyes was brighter now, and his face had softened. She wanted to ask him to wrap his arms around her and hold her while she finished the story, but she knew she couldn't. She'd given up that right when she'd walked away from him yesterday morning. She was sure he hated her for that, because she couldn't feel one ounce of love radiating from him. Why had she run away? Why hadn't she stayed and played it out? Because she'd been afraid, and it had been easier to run away.

She decided to get the story over with so she could leave, because the mixture of pain from the past and knowing that she had lost Sam was crushing her.

"Suddenly, the firing started," she stated hoarsely. "And nearly everyone on the street, including Bill, was shot down. If I'd just screamed out Bill's name the second I realized that there were men with guns surrounding us, I know he could have gotten cover. Just one simple 'Bill,' and he'd still be alive. And that's why I left you, Sam. I was afraid that you'd hate me for being so weak, but I was more afraid that if I was ever in a position where I had to protect you, I wouldn't be able to do it, and that scared me more than you will ever know."

The pain hit Sam unexpectedly when her words, *That's why I left you, Sam,* reverberated through his head. She'd left him. She'd walked away without saying goodbye. She... The hurt was unbearable and he forced himself to shut down. He had to shut everything down, because he couldn't stand the pain.

When he didn't say anything, Liana valiantly wiped the tears off her cheeks and said, "I'll leave now, but so should you. Your mother is very worried about you, Sam. You have to get in touch with her and let her know you're all right. You can't worry your mother at a time like this. She needs you."

Sam was jolted by her words and tears filled his eyes. His mother needed him. She needed him. But how was he supposed to help her when he couldn't seem to help himself?

Liana's heart skipped a beat when she saw tears fill his eyes, and she knew he was almost back. All he needed was a little time alone, and then he'd be all right. At least she'd been able to bring him back, and she'd have to be content with that.

She rose to her feet and said, "I love you, Sam, and I'm sorry I hurt you. If I could do it over again, I'd do everything a lot differently, but I've learned the hard way that you can't change the past."

She knew she shouldn't touch him, but she couldn't resist reaching out and brushing his hair off his forehead. Thankfully, he didn't recoil from her touch. "Goodbye, Sam."

With that she turned and walked away, unaware that Sam was staring after her in bewilderment. For some crazy reason, he wanted to go after her, and he couldn't figure out why. She'd walked away from him without saying goodbye. She'd walked away without telling him why.

But she came back to tell you why, and she came back to tell you goodbye. She loved you enough to come back and give you that much.

Sam practically came out of his skin as the words skipped through his mind, because he would have sworn that it was his grandfather's voice he's heard. But if it was, wouldn't he have felt him? Wouldn't he have known he was here?

Then it hit Sam that he'd been sitting there waiting for his grandfather to come, and he'd been with him all along. The love they'd shared was so special that the old man was a part of his heart, and when his heart spoke, it was echoing both their words. He'd been waiting for him when he'd never really left.

Suddenly, the significance of what his heart had told him sank in. Liana loved him enough to come back and explain. She loved him enough to come back and say goodbye. She loved him enough to share her terrible secret with him.

Incensed anger exploded inside him when her story finally registered. Terrible secret, hell! The man should have been shot for putting her in that kind of danger. How dare he put the woman that he, Samuel Quinten Dillon, loved in mortal danger!

The woman he loved? My, God, the woman he loved had just told him goodbye and walked away, and Sam couldn't believe the reality of the paradox. All these years he'd been torturing himself over the fact that no one had told him goodbye, and now he'd learned how final the word was. Liana was walking away, and if he didn't go after her he might lose her for good!

"Liana!" he yelled as he leaped to his feet, only to fall to his knees as his cramped leg muscles revolted at the sudden movement.

"Liana!" he yelled even louder as he tried to stand again, but a long night of sitting in one position without moving had virtually crippled him.

"Sam, what's wrong?" Liana exclaimed in worried concern as she came running back into the tunnel in time to see him sit down hard and pull his legs up to his chest in an agonized groan.

"What's wrong?" she asked again as she rushed to his side.

"Charley horses," he answered painfully. "Oh, they hurt!"

"Well, here, let me help you," she said as she immediately massaged a leg. "Is it helping?"

"Yes," he whispered as his heart expanded and contracted and expanded again at the sight of her beautiful face turned up to his, and he knew that no matter how bad his legs hurt, his soul hurt more from the need to hold her in his arms.

He reached for her and pulled her to his chest, holding her tight against him. "I love you," he told her, his voice rough with emotion. "I love you, and don't you ever say goodbye and walk away from me again. If you do, I'll . . ."

"You'll what?" Liana asked, levering her head back so she could look up at him, and her heart went wild with joy when she saw that not only was Sam back, but there was love gleaming in his eyes.

"Come after you. Now, help me with my legs, and then we're going to have a long talk about this terrible secret of yours."

SAM DIDN'T WANT to delay their talk, but he knew Liana was right when she said, "We have plenty of time to talk, Sam. Your mother is worried sick. We have to get to a telephone and let her know you're all right."

So the minute he had his legs working again, they made their way down the cliff, with Sam's heart lurching every step of the way when he realized Liana had climbed up it alone. Didn't she know she could have fallen and broken her neck? He decided right then and there that her cliff-climbing days were over.

Back at their cars, he had another heart-lurching experience when he realized he'd have to drive home alone. He kept telling himself that Liana wasn't going to disappear on him again. She'd come after him, hadn't she? So she wouldn't take off.

But all the way back to Denver, he kept an eagle eye on her car, and he only relaxed when they left it at her house and drove to his mother's. He'd called her from the first phone they'd come to on the road, but Liana insisted that they had to go see her so she could personally reassure herself that he was all right.

By the time they got back to his apartment it was nearly dark, and Sam was fairly chomping at the bit to sit her down and talk, but she insisted on feeding him first.

But when she then insisted on doing the dishes, Sam set his foot down. She wasn't going to avoid him any longer.

"No, we're going to talk. The dishes won't go anywhere. Now, come on, Liana," he ordered as he led her into the living room.

Liana nervously rubbed her hand against her thigh as he pushed her down into the sofa and sat beside her. She didn't know why she was so jumpy about talking about her experience in South America. It was apparent that Sam had taken the information in stride.

"First off," Sam said as he wrapped his arm around her and cuddled her to his side, "you weren't weak, Liana. I'm not sure if I could have gotten out a squeak if I'd suddenly realized I was surrounded by armed men."

"But—" she began.

"Just let me finish," he interupted. "Then you can have your say, okay?"

She nodded.

"Secondly, I'd say that the most likely reason why you couldn't react was because you were anticipating danger when you went, which meant you were already afraid. When that fear was confirmed, you froze because you were not trained to function in a potentially volatile situation. And from what you said, I get the impression Bill wasn't either. News people who handle those kinds of incidents are experienced, trained professionals, not young whippersnappers out to make themselves a name, and a trained professional would have never taken you along in the first place.

"Thirdly," he went on, "I have no doubt that you'd lay your life down for me, because you did it today when you climbed that cliff. You could have fallen and broken your neck, but you didn't even think about it once, let alone twice, did you?"

"Of course not. I knew you were in pain and I had to get to you."

"Exactly, and if you ever do something like that again, I'll throttle you," he said as he put his hands around her neck and gave her a playful shake. Then he sobered and said, "Now, tell me what you're feeling about Bill and South America."

"I don't know." She released a heavy sigh and rested her head against his shoulder. "For so long I've carried the guilt that it's hard to let it go. And it's the horror of seeing someone I loved violently killed that eats at me. But I'm also angry, Sam. There's a part of me that's very angry at Bill not only for getting us into that mess in the first place, but leaving me to make my own escape and forcing me to deal with the government all by myself when I got back home. Since I was an eye witness, I was grilled for weeks for details, so I was forced to relive the nightmare over and over again. They told me that it was important information for national security, and I think that was the only thing that kept me from going completely over the edge. At least I could tell myself that Bill's death wasn't totally senseless."

She sighed again as she said, "My parents say Bill used me, and I still can't accept that. I want to believe he loved me as much as I loved him, and if I come to the conclusion that he didn't, then I think I'm going to become even angrier." She tilted her head so she could look up at him. "I think the best way to describe how I feel is that I'm very confused."

"Maybe you should seek some counseling," Sam suggested.

"I know I should, and I should have done it three years ago. But then again, if I'd done that, I might not have met you, and that scares me to death."

She reached up and tenderly stroked his beard-stubbled cheek. "I loved Bill, Sam. I really did. But what I feel for you is so much more intense. It nearly killed me to leave you yesterday, and when I came looking for you last night and couldn't find you, I nearly went out of my mind. But when I found you in the tunnel and you looked so empty, I felt...I can't even think of a word to describe how I felt. All I knew was that I had to bring you back, because I loved you too much to see you suffering like that."

"Now, you know how I felt when I was dealing with you," he told her gruffly and gave her a squeeze. "I also have to say that I loved Kay, and when she walked away it hurt. Really hurt. But when you left me, I wanted to lie down and die, because like you, my love for you is so much more intense. In light of that, let's make a pact. From this moment on, no more hiding our feelings, regardless of how painful they are."

"It's a deal," Liana said. "And let's start by you telling me what you're feeling about your grandfather's death."

Sam gave a thoughtful shake of his head. "When I realized yesterday that he wouldn't be there for me anymore, I came apart. But when you walked out of the tunnel after telling me goodbye, I thought I heard him talk to me. Then I realized that it was really my own heart talking, and because the love he and I shared was so special, he's a part of my heart and will always be there for me. I'll miss him, but I'll never lose him. Since I've accepted that, I can accept that he's gone."

"That's a beautiful way to deal with it," Liana said as she reached up to swipe at the tears that had begun to roll down her cheeks as she listened to his words.

"Don't ever wipe away your tears. I love your tears," Sam said as he caught her hand and kissed them away. When he was done, he said, "I love you, Liana. I want to spend the rest of my life with you. It's time for a change of seasons for both of us, so will you marry me and share the beauty of spring with me?"

"Yes, Sam. Oh, yes," Liana replied fervently and threw her arms around his neck.

When he touched his lips to hers, everything inside her burst into bloom, because she knew that if winter ever touched her again, Sam would always be there to guide her back into spring. But, then again, she'd always be there to guide him back, too.

Silhouette Sensation

COMING NEXT MONTH

A TALENT FOR LOVE
Saranne Dawson

When Tori Wentworth had a vision of violence, her
police chief brother-in-law was glad of the help she
could give him. Then a man who looked like the
possible murderer came to town and he was certain
Tori knew his secret.

Matt was drawn to Tori and it was more than just her
psychic abilities that attracted him. She didn't really
believe he was the murderer ... did she?

BELOVED DREAMER
Anne Henry

Julie was engaged to a man who promised security,
prestige and an end to scrimping and saving. But
Julie wondered what she would do if Chad Morgan
asked her to go away with him. He'd asked her years
ago and for all those years Julie had been dreaming
of what might have been, wondering what had
become of him.

Now she knew. Here he was, large as life. This time
could she sacrifice everything for love?

Silhouette Sensation

COMING NEXT MONTH

A PERILOUS EDEN
Heather Graham Pozzessere

Right from the first Amber had been attracted to the enigmatic stranger; she knew he was dangerous and her father had indirectly confirmed it. The passion the couple shared on a sultry tropical cruise was hot, steamy — complete. But that was before Amber became the prisoner of ruthless terrorists …

Adams wanted revenge and Amber had been in the way and was now in mortal jeopardy. He would need all his skill and daring to save her — and all his strength to walk away from her.

FLIRTING WITH DANGER
Linda Turner

Sheer terror had driven heiress Gabriella Winters to flee her family home in the dead of night. A frightening encounter aboard a freight train led to rescue by a dark, handsome stranger called Austin LePort.

LePort had been riding the rails for weeks researching his latest book. But Gabriella was his most interesting find. Still, Austin was a loner and he didn't need a companion, especially an infuriating, irritating, vulnerable *virgin!*

COMING NEXT MONTH FROM

Silhouette

Desire

*provocative, sensual love stories
for the woman of today*

GLORY, GLORY Linda Lael Miller
LOOKING FOR TROUBLE Nancy Martin
THE BRIDAL PRICE Barbara Boswell
UPON A MIDNIGHT CLEAR Laura Leone
THE PENDRAGON VIRUS Cait London
HANDSOME DEVIL Joan Hohl

Special Edition

*longer, satisfying romances with
mature heroines and lots of emotion*

THE LAST GOOD MAN ALIVE Myrna Temte
ONE LOST WINTER Diana Whitney
AGAINST ALL ODDS Joleen Daniels
DOUBLE DARE Christine Rimmer
SHADOWS ON THE SAND Maggi Charles
SWEET LIES, SATIN SIGHS Bay Matthews